"Medicine on a Grand Scale": Rudolf Virchow, Liberalism, and the Public Health

Ian F McNeely

The Wellcome Trust Centre for the History of Medicine at
University College London
Occasional Publication, No. 1

Contents

Acknowledgements

This little book originated as my 1992 honours thesis at Harvard. I thank the Wellcome Trust Centre for enabling me to publish it, in updated form, ten years later. I would also like to recognize those who encouraged me, personally and intellectually, along the way: Jeff Richter, Nathan Stoltzfus, Kevin Bolan, Michael Sang Yun Kim, Bob Berle, Patricia Lynch, John Patterson, Andrew Scull, and Lisa Wolverton. The Harvard Center for European Studies generously funded my research in Berlin. I dedicate this work to my father, a physician, and to my mother, a liberal.

Chapter 1

Medicine, Politics, and Liberalism
in the Career of Rudolf Virchow

"Medicine is a social science, and politics is nothing more than medicine on a grand scale".[1] In this celebrated statement, the nineteenth-century German physician Rudolf Virchow (1821–1902) summarized his belief in the utter inseparability of medicine from politics. Virchow regarded medicine not merely as the study of human disease but as a general metaphor for understanding society. What most people regarded as medicine *per se* – the treatment of illness and the alleviation of suffering – was actually a microcosm of Medicine in the grand sense, which took society as its patient. Just as medicine in the everyday sense provided the stethoscopes and scalpels by which to elucidate and rectify individual sickness, so Medicine in Virchow's sense could rely on rigorous investigation and decisive intervention to cure social ills. Just as medicine embraced a moral concern for the well-being and happiness of individuals in suffering, so Medicine dictated that the political system had an ethical obligation to improve the health and material condition of the less fortunate in society. The politician and the physician, if not one and the same, at least had the responsibility to co-operate in applying political salves to societal wounds.

Rudolf Virchow lived during a formative time, both in the political life of his nation and in the development of German medicine. He witnessed the founding of the German Empire, and the rise of Bismarck's Prussia to become the leading power of Continental Europe, as well as Robert Koch's bacteriological theory of disease, which made it possible to locate the bacilli for tuberculosis and cholera. Virchow himself made an astounding number of contributions to both medicine and politics. His reputation rests, first and foremost, on his seminal achievements in medical science. Medical students still memorize Virchow's Triad to help them diagnose blood clots, and consumers of pork can thank him for having discovered the parasite for trichinosis. By far his most important work was in pathology, a discipline he revolutionized. Virchow's canonical textbook, *Cellular Pathology*, argued that cells arise only from other cells, not from spontaneous generation, and that the study of disease should focus on cellular abnormalities. His

5

pathbreaking contention that the cell is the fundamental unit of life has only recently been extended by the rise of the gene.

A rigorous empiricist, Virchow resisted endorsing Darwinism in the absence of concrete and convincing research; a committed humanist, he wrote a book extolling Goethe's work as a student of nature. Virchow saw no contradiction in combining these identities. Medicine, for him, effortlessly reconciled hard-nosed science and ethical humanism. Virchow regarded medicine as a *social* science and devoted tremendous energy to disciplines he saw as its natural adjuncts in the empirical study of human beings, principally archaeology and physical anthropology. He excavated with Schliemann at Troy and helped acquire vast ancient treasures for the museums in Berlin. He edited Germany's most important scholarly journal of ethnology. Most famously, Virchow supervised a study of seven million German schoolchildren disproving the existence of a predominantly blond-haired, blue-eyed Aryan racial type.[2] He also amassed a collection of four thousand carefully measured skulls and used them, similarly, to dispute the correlation between race and cranial capacity.

Among what he saw as the social sciences, politics offered Virchow the richest opportunities to practise medicine on a grand scale. His activities in politics were as impressive as his dedication to the various branches of empirical investigation. He manned the barricades in the 1848 Revolution, helped found the German Progressive Party, tangled with Bismarck during the founding of the Reich, and sat for ninety-six years of combined, concurrent service to local, regional, and national German parliaments. Virchow also famously coined the term *Kulturkampf*, a "struggle of civilizations", to describe, favourably, the German State's assault on the Catholic Church in the 1870s. Not surprisingly, Virchow attempted to connect his interests in medicine and politics, and through his achievements developed a practical philosophy to explain their interaction. In his writings he advocated a co-operation between doctors and statesmen aimed at securing the health of citizens in the broadest possible matrix of their social and political interactions. Through his concrete interventions, he capitalized on the possibilities of this politicized medicine in such fields as sanitation, epidemiology, professional reform, forensic medicine, hospital construction, medical statistics and medical welfare legislation.

Contemporary scholarship has barely penetrated the meaning of Virchow's famous utterance and of his medical politics in general. Some writers view "medicine on a grand scale" merely as an inspirational slogan. Leon Eisenberg extols Virchow's willingness to defend health care as an ethical right and to pursue its realization on a political level.[3] Daniel Pridian explains that this personal crusade arose from Virchow's belief that the social bases of disease – poverty, ignorance and oppression – needed a political remedy, just as the biological factors needed a strictly biomedical one.[4] Both Eisenberg and Pridian are just two examples of a much more general tendency towards hagiography in accounts of Virchow's contribution to medical politics. Other scholars regard Virchow more suspiciously, taking his bold statement as a literal political principle. Karl Figlio views Virchow's bid to extend medicine into social affairs as an instance of scientist politics; the encroachment of medicine into social diagnosis and cure "might have brought a technocratic, authoritarian state" in which doctors were "the experts to run society on scientific principles". Paul Weindling argues for Virchow's professional self-interest from another perspective, maintaining that Virchow in fact endorsed absolute freedom of physicians from state control, so that "doctors should be free from social accountability".[5] In this conception, Virchow's grand pronouncements on medicine and politics were merely the smokescreen for a deeper professional arrogance.

Erwin Ackerknecht's 1953 study is by far the best complete biography of Virchow in German or in English and treats his medical and political ideas completely separately. It remains indispensable as a guide to Virchow's activities as a doctor, statesman, and anthropologist.[6] However, in discussing these identities independently and in succession, Ackerknecht cannot fully convey how his subject conceived of them as parts of a unified life's work. Virchow lived at a time when science and politics were only just coming to be seen as separate vocations.[7] Many of his bitterest conflicts with contemporaries stemmed, in part, from his controversial attempts to apply the same standards and values to both fields. Virchow's frictions with Bismarck, who once challenged him to a duel over a perceived insult to his honour, show this quite clearly. Bismarck saw Virchow as a dreamy professor, an idealist, an interloper. Referring to him in the Prussian parliament, Bismarck noted: "Politics is not an exact science ... I fully recognize the prominence of the speaker in his field of expertise [but] since [he] has amateurishly stepped out of his field and into mine, I must say that his politics strikes me as lightweight".[8] At a time of ongoing professionalization, Virchow blithely overstepped not only the disciplinary boundaries within science, but also the profoundly political divisions between science and society at large. Any approach to his life that compartmentalizes his achievement leaves unanswered the critical question of how, in Virchow's view, science should inform politics, and vice versa.

A more promising approach, and one that I favour, interprets Virchow's dictum in the context of his lifelong liberalism. In this view, the analogy Virchow made between medicine and politics reflected a deep ideological conviction that liberalism provided a common basis for each. Virchow's theory of a "cell-state", for instance, drew parallels between the human body, composed of equally viable cells, and the body politic, consisting of

7

individuals enjoying equal rights.[9] More generally, his commitment to free scientific discourse and an open, multi-causal account of disease can be seen as the inspiration behind a political programme embracing democracy, pluralism, rational education, secularism and other liberal values.[10] Medicine on a grand scale, in this conception, meant rigorously applying the liberal values enshrined by medical science on a political level. This approach recognizes Virchow's positive contribution to German liberalism, while also acknowledging its weaknesses. Sometimes, Virchow's medical values steered his politics towards precisely the kind of dictatorial scientism feared by his critics. Thus, during the *Kulturkampf*, his worship of scientific reason led him to support the German State's patently illiberal repression of the Catholic Church as a crusade against superstition. At other times, Virchow deployed his scientific insight to vindicate the humane values so cherished by his admirers. Most notably, in his dispute with Ernst Haeckel, Germany's leading proponent of Darwinism, Virchow assailed the empirical basis of evolutionary theory to undermine the idea that natural selection favours an undemocratic social hierarchy.[11]

Virchow's liberalism married a robust, substantive set of political claims with a subtly yet distinctly partisan approach to the ascertainment of scientific truth. Unlike many present-day liberals, he did not, in other words, treat politics as a neutral space embodying no particular conception of the good life, or cordon off science as a value-free arena for the professionally disinterested adjudication of empirical claims.[12] Like nineteenth-century liberals in general, Virchow lived in a world where liberalism was one ideology among many, not a framework for all the others. Like German liberals in particular, he confronted this fact through hard experience. German liberalism, to an unusual degree, competed for hegemony with rival ideologies like socialism, conservatism, and, later, radical nationalism – all very articulate philosophies, each with its own political apparatus and scientific proponents.[13] That Virchow had to contend with such rivals helps explain why his scientific and political activity frequently took the form, not of incremental practical reforms, but of sweeping ideological crusades. Virchow often utterly failed to recognize that he was engaged in contests over ideology, not truth. Yet for this very reason, a purely ideological analysis of his work and thought cannot account for the many practical successes his crusades achieved. To assess what Virchow's liberalism truly implied requires an attention to the specifically medical projects (as opposed to the grander ideological undertakings) in which his politics and his science actively intertwined. In fact, Virchow's willingness to undertake mundane activities in health care reform demands such an approach. After all, it was precisely in these smaller-scale arenas that medicine on a grand scale would find actual, and not merely metaphorical, application.

8

To give this historical context more concrete meaning I have chosen three particularly revealing episodes from Virchow's life. Chapter Two deals with Virchow's political awakening in 1848, when he was sent to observe an epidemic then raging in the poverty-stricken Prussian district of Upper Silesia. Newly sensitized to the social causes of disease through this experience, Virchow developed the belief that "medicine on a grand scale" required political regeneration along liberal lines. Rushing back to Berlin, Virchow found in the 1848 Revolution the opportunity to refine his philosophy through the so-called "medical reform" movement, in which physicians attempted to improve their professional condition through liberal political activity. Far from narrowly serving their own interests, as Weindling suggests, the medical reformers sought a more activist and significant role in the liberal regeneration of society. This revolutionary context nurtured Virchow's medical politics at the same time as it ultimately condemned his activities to political failure. Liberalism's defeat forced Virchow to retrench and pursue health care reform in a less revolutionary and less ambitious, but still liberal, political context.

Chapter Three discusses Virchow's successful attempt to find a more congenial context for the realization of medical politics through his participation in the construction of Berlin's sewer system. Through his detailed medical research and his prominence as a city councilman, Virchow provided both the scientific backing and public health justification necessary to implement the "canalization" project, but he also owed an enormous debt to the political power of urban liberalism in Germany and in Berlin specifically. What appears to be a completely apolitical undertaking – sanitation reform – was actually a rallying point for liberals who sought to transform the cities into enclaves of political power. Public health reforms not only enhanced the image of cities dominated by liberal politicians, but also seemed to validate the tenets of liberal ideology itself. While tangibly improving the living conditions of every inhabitant, such reforms otherwise preserved social relations and avoided radical redistributions of wealth. Owing to their technical nature and only indirect social impact, projects like canalization were thus appropriate reforms for an ambitious liberal municipal government to undertake. Tracing the obstacles and opportunities in capturing sewerage reform as the province of urban liberalism, and elucidating Virchow's relationship to this effort, constitutes the true subject of my third chapter.

If municipal politics remained a bastion of liberal influence in medical affairs for Virchow, parliamentary politics was a source of frustration. Chapter Four takes his parliamentary activity in medical politics as an opportunity to discuss the broader possibilities for health care reform in Imperial Germany. In a variety of areas ranging from national sickness insurance legislation to Koch's bacteriological theory of disease, political and professional developments conspired to restrict the scope of the interventionist social medicine espoused by Virchow. To be sure, the founding of the German Empire in 1871 gave medical reformers an unprecedented opportunity – in the form of a unified and powerful state – to sponsor nationwide health care projects. The consolidation and increasing influence of the German medical profession in these same years gave health care reformers like Virchow the benefit of a corps of physicians to carry the burden of practical activity. However, the conservative character of the new empire and the medical profession's turn towards narrow interest group politics diminished the chances for Virchowian liberalism. Chapter Four therefore argues that Virchow's marginalization was not simply the product of his dogmatic adherence to liberal democratic principles after their partial eclipse in Bismarck's Reich, but arose more generally from the inability to pursue health reform in a political environment that had in some ways transcended liberalism.

A clear pattern emerges in these episodes, tying Virchow's pursuit of medical politics to the broader fortunes of liberalism in nineteenth-century Germany. Put simply, Virchow's liberalism succeeded in municipal politics but failed on the national level both in 1848 and in Bismarck's Empire. In this pattern of success and failure, Virchow's career exemplified the predicaments of a liberal social scientist. In each of the three different historical contexts treated below, the outlook of this peculiar political hybrid provides a model connecting Virchow's liberalism to his medical politics. When liberalism was still a combative creed, not yet a neutral ideology, the social science it inspired took on an overtly reformist cast. The primary thrust of liberal social science was thus to reconstitute society in order to bring it in line with liberal principles. In Virchow's case these principles emphasized individual rights (including health), democratic government, science and reason, and education. The liberal social scientist also had a commitment to avoid revolutionary expropriation and socially subversive programmes that threatened the limited goals towards which liberal reformism aspires. It might be necessary to employ radical means to implement reform, but these means must not threaten the moderate ends at the heart of liberalism.

This need for containment is the crucial dilemma of liberal social science – one less apparent, though equally present, in its more anodyne twenty-first-century incarnation – and Virchow wrestled with it repeatedly in his medical politics. Very early on, it led him to develop two abiding commitments that continually thrust him into contact with the political forces around him. First, Virchow advocated the empowerment of a social class that would carry the banner of reform and moderate its subversive potential. At times he identified this élite as the educated bourgeoisie, but more provocatively, he lauded his own profession as the standard-bearer of liberalism and progress. Second, Virchow implicitly and explicitly invoked the power of a liberal state to channel and direct the energies of a reformist élite, and to ensure social stability in the process. This notion may seem incongruous in a man who has been called a "libertarian",[14] but Virchow's animosity towards the German State as it was constituted in the nineteenth century, and his desire to free society from its clutches, did not cause him to reject the concept of a powerful state in itself. It simply meant that his ideals could not always find expression within the political realities he confronted, whether in Berlin or in the empire as a whole.

By casting Virchow as a liberal social scientist I hope to demonstrate his belonging in the broad political movement of German liberalism in a more fundamental way than a simple reference to his personal ideological programme implies. An ideological definition of liberalism is in fact quite difficult in this context. In nineteenth-century Germany, the term "liberal" encompassed a spectrum of opinions ranging from *laissez-faire* to protectionist in the economic sphere, Lutheran to atheist in religious matters, and libertarian to statist in the realm of politics.[15] Part of the aim of this study is to demonstrate how liberalism embraced many shades of opinion, while remaining a movement in which Virchow's programme could still find deep resonance. By stepping into practical activity, Virchow donned the mantle of scientific social reform and became subject to its inherent tensions. This argument and the method it entails will, I hope, avoid an overreliance on Virchow's personal beliefs and accomplishments in explaining his career. By placing him within the company of other liberals in Germany, and in particular of those who helped define the nature of liberal politics through their reformist undertakings, I want to suggest that Virchow's exceptionalism did not so much make him an anomaly in the world of Bismarckian *Realpolitik* as it attested to the vitality of certain elements within German liberalism. There is only so much that one man's life can tell us about the group to which he belongs, but in conclusion I situate Virchow's liberal reformism in the context of his contemporaries, suggesting that his vitality argues for a more complex approach to a movement whose political failure has been overdrawn and somewhat unfairly portrayed in the historical literature.

Chapter 2

Virchow's Revolutionary Years, 1848–9: Medicine and Politics as Liberal Social Science

A life full of work and toil is not a burden but a blessing ... It is by incessant work that we learn about real life; it is thus that we gather over the years a far richer store of experiences and draw on deep, unfathomable treasures of wisdom accessible only to the initiated and not to lazy and idle persons given to rest and ease.[16]

A seventeen-year-old Virchow wrote these words in his 1839 graduation examination from the Köslin Gymnasium in his native Pomerania, now part of northwestern Poland. The next decade of his life bore concrete witness to Virchow's belief in work and toil as the privilege of an enlightened, "initiated" élite. His first love would always be medicine, and later in 1839 he embraced the "blessing" that a difficult medical career had to offer. On scholarship to the Friedrich-Wilhelm-Institut in Berlin, established in 1795 to train gifted young men to become army doctors, Virchow's work and toil was at first very unexceptional for a student in his position. He constantly worried about finances; he struggled to overcome the chaos and indiscipline of medical education at the time, unlike some students whose main interests were "skipping lessons, playing cards [and] drinking beer"; and he bemoaned the poor socio-economic status of doctors, complaining that railroad workers could earn as much in a day as doctors did in a month. Finally, he had to deal with the strictly medical cares thrust upon him as a would-be physician, which included such activities as "the administration of laxatives, sleeping powders [and] toothache pills" as well as the occasional blood-letting and application of leeches. In 1846, Virchow completed his last state medical examinations, began giving lectures in pathological anatomy (a science he later revolutionized), and embarked on the practice of medicine as a fully-fledged physician.[17]

Virchow's initiation into the world of medicine coincided with a developing interest in a second realm, that of politics. By the late 1840s he was writing to his father of the "violent" debates in the Prussian parliament and the decline of the government's legitimacy. Of particular importance in the "hungry forties" was the so-called social question. This issue, regarding what should be done to check the moral and material decline of the country's lower classes, was a matter of increasing political concern for the German educated public. Virchow noted that in such circumstances "a harvest too can be a political event", and expressed a special interest in observing the typhus epidemic in Upper Silesia, an outbreak in which the Silesians' poverty and destitution had been implicated. Virchow would eventually combine his twin interests in medicine and politics in investigating this "scandal that has become full-blown by the death of thousands".[18] For the time being, however, he continued to view political events from the "domestic" confines of the Charité, Berlin's largest hospital, which he likened to a "town of its own", isolated from the outside world.[19]

Virchow's work brought him into contact with patients whose physical ailments paralleled the material and psychological suffering that characterized the lower classes as a whole, a fact that constrained him to view the social question through the prism of personal medical experience. In 1843 he wrote to his father of the stench and dirt and high temperatures in the scabies wards, whose inmates came from the "most depraved level of society". He also described insane patients in whose hearts "distrust and suspicion reign supreme", and who exhibited religious mysticism and a predilection for masturbation.[20] Virchow's attitude towards these people mixed sympathy and disgust. On the one hand he likened himself to a "jailer" of the human wrecks who wound up in the Charité. On the other, he thoroughly enjoyed his work and commented that it "makes both me and my patients happy, for my nurse constantly assures me that I am much too good to them".[21] Above all, Virchow saw these people through the eyes of a doctor. Though the discipline of medicine at that time did not enjoy the heroic mystique that it does today, it none the less conferred on its practitioners the unique opportunity to mingle among the afflicted without joining them, to practise charity and administer healing from a comfortable professional distance. Virchow's remarks on this subject reveal a kernel of human compassion within a thick coating of scientific objectivity. He remarked clinically but tellingly that his medical experiences had introduced him to "the most interesting personalities", and that through them, "one's knowledge of human nature is greatly enriched".[22]

This blend of compassion and distance would come to characterize Virchow's medical politics as a whole, but it took the experiences of the revolutionary years 1848–9 to channel these inklings of social concern into a coherent ideology. During this period, Virchow's ethic of work and toil found expression in a realm beyond personal cultivation, inspiring a political crusade through which he honed a liberal approach to the social question. This chapter aims to demonstrate how Virchow applied his newly acquired "treasures" of medical wisdom to social politics, which subjected him to the logic of the liberal social scientist. Though it would be going too far to single out Virchow's medical experience as the sole determinant of his peculiarly liberal beliefs, there is none the less a firm connection between his professionalized compassion in the medical realm, and his paternalistic ideology in the political realm. Medical practice combined social distance with fraternal humanism in the relationship of doctor to patient, and to Virchow this relationship paralleled that between liberal social scientists and the suffering masses. From his superior vantage point, he strove to heal the people by elevating them to a social and political level he deemed "healthy". The strategy of co-opting the disenfranchised into a stable order based on equal rights, education, rule of law, democracy, personal freedom and scientific rationality formed the outlines of Virchow's social politics. To achieve these aims would entail a social revolution, but one whose explosive potential must be moderated by a reformist élite exercising its power through a benevolent state.

The lineaments of the liberal social scientist:
Virchow in Upper Silesia

Virchow's liberal ideology of social politics was crystallized by his observation of the Upper Silesian typhus epidemic. By all accounts, the experience fundamentally changed his life, stirring in him an appreciation for the social and political causes of disease. Sent by the Prussian Minister of Culture to report on the medical conditions of the epidemic, Virchow arrived in the Silesian village of Sohrau, in what is today south-eastern Poland, on 24 February 1848.[23] His first impression of the area was not of any particular medical condition, but rather of the general debasement of the population, which had rendered it susceptible to epidemic onslaughts. Virchow wrote evocatively of the Silesians' poverty, describing the shabbiness of their living arrangements, their poor eating habits, and their utter lack of hygiene. Plagued by "vermin" and lice, the Upper Silesian "leaves it to celestial providence to free his body occasionally by a heavy shower of rain from the crusts of dirt accumulated on it".[24] The "slavish and submissive" Silesians cared more for brandy and sexual licentiousness than discipline and hard work, in Virchow's opinion. They had no conception of private property and no concern for thrift or planning ahead, nor did they have a strong family structure. Their "canine subservience" and utter contempt for middle-class values reinforced Virchow's belief that only "a free man accustomed to work" could serve as a model citizen, and that such a man, on viewing the Silesian people, could not help but "feel disgust rather than pity".[25]

Despite the vehemence of his revulsion, Virchow strove to understand and characterize the Silesians in more scientific terms and attempted to acquire the professional distance necessary for a more objective analysis.

His meticulous description of their living quarters informs us that the dimensions of a typical house were 8 to 12 feet (2.4 to 3.7 metres) square and 5 to 6 feet (1.5 to 1.8 metres) high, and that from 1834 to 1847, the average number of inhabitants per house increased from 7.5 to 9.5.[26] More importantly, Virchow determined to ferret out the medical causes of the epidemic with rigorous scientific methods. Through case studies as well as statistical evidence he explored in excruciating detail the urinary and fecal discharges, dermatological eruptions, and pained respirations of typhus patients. His clinical descriptions in the meaty middle section of the report stand in marked contrast to the excited outbursts of the beginning.[27]

Virchow evaluated these empirical findings in light of contemporary theories on contagion and infection, the influence of climate and geography, the distinction between typhus and typhoid, and the role of "miasmas" and decaying vegetation in the etiology of the epidemic. His conclusion emphasized a miasma that he took to be the endemic cause of the disease and that stemmed mainly from factors like "chemical decomposition" as well as moisture and other weather conditions. He explicitly denied any monocausal connection between typhus and the poor housing conditions in Silesia, starvation or poor diet, or bad hygiene, but made room for the possibility that social circumstances could be contributory factors. Famine, for instance, "might have increased the predisposition for the disease"; and the "unwholesome circumstances" connected with the Silesians' living conditions could have produced that crucial, marginal difference in susceptibility that transformed an endemic miasma into a disease of epidemic proportions. This is what Virchow meant when he wrote that "we have always felt obliged to seek the cause of an epidemic in . . . an intensification of domestic insalubrity".[28]

This conclusion gave Virchow the opportunity to analyse the social determinants of disease in more detail than the simple descriptions of "domestic insalubrity" entailed. By upholding such social determinants as valid scientific cofactors in disease etiology, Virchow sought to transform his impressionistic criticisms of the Silesian population into more precise (but hardly less polemical) formulations of social underdevelopment. In so framing his ideas, he applied his professional perspective to a far-reaching solution of the social questions bedeviling Silesia, and styled himself the physician-reformer diagnosing society's ills.

The first social factor he isolated concerned the withering of ethnic identity among the population. Silesia, he explained, had been severed from the mother Poland for over 700 years, and while the Lower Silesians had been almost completely Germanized, the Upper Silesians had retained Polish customs and language and thus remained outsiders when Prussia obtained control over the region. The result was a population adrift, with no Polish

(handwritten: British population too)

role models and no national consciousness, and therefore "in a dreadful way... no development and no culture".[29] To the extent that Polish influences remained in Silesia, their effect was primarily negative. Virchow cited here the pernicious tenacity of the Catholic religion among the Silesians, showing an anticlerical streak that would later mark his behaviour during the *Kulturkampf.* He derided the parish priest, whom he labelled the "absolute master" of his congregation, and alleged that the Catholic hierarchy, in order to maintain its power, sought "to keep the people bigoted, stupid, and dependent". Catholic charity during the epidemic he regarded as erratic, poorly coordinated, and concerned with "individual patients only, and not the epidemic as a whole". To a thoroughly secular man like Virchow, Catholicism could not help but induce submissiveness, fatalism, obscurantism and "mental bondage" in its adherents, at the same time as it failed its Christian calling to succour its flock.[30]

Economically, the Silesians remained mired in the Polish institution of "robotage" or quasi-serfdom. The rendering of five to six days service per week by *robots* sapped them of the individual initiative and personal zest necessary to vitalize the economy, improve social conditions, and reduce the population's proclivity towards disease. Moreover, the stratified nature of Upper Silesian society distanced the classes from one another and prevented any meaningful cooperation between them. Echoing Marx, Virchow decried the appearance of a "young money aristocracy" that had abandoned its traditional duties towards the populace. There existed a dearth of leading citizens and educated men to harness the potential of the Silesian people, because in this region the few educated people there were had become acclimatized to the suffering around them. Many proposals for sickness relief, Virchow noted, generated "a general complaint that the people would be spoilt". The absence of a dedicated phalanx of socially conscious and prosperous citizens meant that for the lower classes, "no one was there to act as their friend, their teacher, or their guardian".[31]

The combination of cultural waywardness, religious oppression, and class tension had produced a catastrophe of such proportions, according to Virchow, that "never during the 33 years of peace in Germany had even remotely similar conditions been seen".[32] In his mind, the situation called for thorough and immediate change. Virchow did not hesitate to pile on the most radical prescriptions to cure the Silesians of the deeper social factors that had predisposed them to epidemics. He called first of all for "full and unlimited democracy", and in consideration of Silesia's special status, national self-determination and a complete release from Prussian rule. These remedies would allow the Silesians to evolve indigenous institutions of government at the same time as they joined "the great family of Slav peoples". Nurturing this awakening in the new Silesia would be the liberal triad of wealth, education and freedom, which Virchow regarded as direct substitutes for the "hunger, ignorance, and servitude" he found there at the time.[33] To achieve these liberal ends Virchow admitted the potential necessity of violent means. He noted that the powers that be are never willing to admit that a people is "ripe" for self-determination, so sometimes the people have to take matters into their own hands. Thus, though he deplored the rule of "fire and sword", he believed that in an imperfect world they could be the instruments of "a high ethical and human elevation".[34]

Such a heroic cure brought with it the danger that the patient would react violently. Lest the Silesians' revolutionary fire take on the character of a "glowing fanaticism", Virchow proposed that a concerned body of social reformers and "great men of state" involve itself in the elevation of the people, channelling their fiery zeal into a "mild but enduring and fecundating warmth".[35] Meritocratically selected and drawn from the educated indigenous population, such leaders would lead the people into prosperity by means of a "tutelary control", thus "awakening their dormant qualities". They would replace the oppressive Catholic hierarchy and insensitive aristocracy whose anachronistic rule then passed for leadership, and constitute the class that would bear the standard of liberty and entice the people to share in its advantages.[36] Despite their salutary influence, however, these reformers could not in themselves consolidate and manage the social revolution that Virchow prescribed. In medicine, the healer can rely on biological mechanisms to effect his remedy, but in statecraft, the reformer depends on the artificial power of government to implement change. A managed social reform in fact demanded a context through which democratic institutions and personal liberties could be established and protected, and the role of the state in providing this context is the most challenging aspect of the Silesian report.

Not surprisingly, Virchow found the current state apparatus hopelessly anachronistic and rooted in the bureaucratic-absolutist traditions of mid-nineteenth-century Prussia. He faulted the bureaucracy for being too repressive and authoritarian. The paper-pushing officialdom, with its deadening centralization, surveillance mentality, and "patronizing and artificial formalism" had made a mockery of the famed Prussian civil service. Virchow betrayed his utter contempt for the bureaucratic state when he wrote to his father that

sum after sum is spent, official follows official, extra posts lie in heaps in the fathomless mud of these highways – but the dead do not come back to life, and many people will retain the germs of an endless illness ... And yet the government still does nothing more than send flour and here and there a physician, and use up a lot of paper in writing. It is horrible, disgusting.[37]

The good government, on the other hand, did not demolish bureaucracy *per se*, but rather established it on a more rational footing. A vigorous local self-government should replace an administration "estranged from the requirements of the people" and guided by rigid ordinances instead of local contingencies. In the stimulation of "a common general effort" among the people, the ideal government would undertake practical projects, like road-building, improvement of agriculture and animal husbandry, and regulation of industrial competition and exploitation.[38]

The virtue of such a government, and the feature that distinguished it from the Prussian ideal of an enlightened but paternalistic bureaucracy, would be its collaboration with a coequal, local civil society. In an immature society such as Silesia's, however, only the state itself could provide the basis for such a partnership. To cultivate vitality in the social sphere, the state must intervene decisively to secure the "unquestionable right to a healthy life". This presumed, first of all, material and moral elevation. Through education and the bestowal of rights, the state could make the people "not only externally free but even more so internally".[39] But Virchow doubted that "constitutionalism" and schooling alone could effect the changes he required. He criticized the "absurd concentration of capital and landed property" in the hands of a few individuals, and thus advocated associations of the unpropertied as counterweights to the privileges of capital, maintaining that a more equitable distribution of wealth was "the sole means of improving the social condition". Importantly, however, he rejected large-scale state employment of labour as a "new factor in the subjugation and dependence of the individual". A lively associational life, an interplay of the interests of capital and the interests of labour: these recommendations seemed more democratic than any socialistic enterprise the state might undertake.[40] Virchow's liberal philosophy thus specified clear limits on the extension of state power – even when such power was aimed at securing the very ideals of liberalism itself.

Virchow's ambivalence about state intervention is clearest in his advocacy of public health reform. Owing to his medical outlook, he regarded such reform as the centrepiece of any programme of social politics. Again criticizing the status quo, Virchow found state physicians to be contemptibly ignorant of science and submissive to authority. What was needed was a better-trained corps of physician-reformers, acquainted with epidemiological principles, who could produce "long, detailed studies of local conditions" in their regions. Such studies would serve as the scientific basis for the formulation of legislation that would address the public health concerns of the nation.[41] To prevent future epidemics, the state must take its cue from medical experts and intervene to protect society. As Virchow diagnosed the Silesian case, "with 1.5 million people, palliatives will no longer do. If we wish to take remedial action we must be radical".[42] As to the precise mechanisms mediating between medical expert knowledge and concrete social policy, however, Virchow said nothing. That a scientistic dictatorship of medicine could threaten the freedoms and pluralism of democracy was not a concern of his – at least not yet. What was important was simply that the state should formulate a social policy based on scientific principles. Since "medicine has imperceptibly led us into the social field", it was the responsibility of physicians to provide the "theoretical solution" and politicians the "actual solution" of social problems.[43] Medicine was central to the social question, and therefore had political claims on the state. But having drawn the state into the "actual solution", Virchow went no further in articulating its ideal form. In the Silesian report, Virchow simply provided the most schematic outlines of a state apparatus designed for radically reformist purposes but treading a fine line between bureaucratic paternalism and social partnership, state intervention and individual rights, and medical knowledge and democratic government.

The 1848 revolution: liberal politics and medical reform

The next fifteen months drew Virchow closer to exact formulations by subjecting his ideas to the test of political practice as he participated, as a liberal and a physician, in the 1848 revolution. If Virchow developed the basic principles of his lifelong political philosophy in the remoteness of Upper Silesia, he found in the concentrated excitement of Berlin the active give-and-take of public discourse. On 10 March 1848, he hurried back from Silesia to the capital, where the next day he found it "highly disturbed". On the 18th, the revolution in Berlin took on a popular character when Prussian troops fired two shots into a crowd gathered outside the royal palace, sending the mob into a frenzy. In a letter written to his father the next day, Virchow described the noise of cannons and the construction of barricades that had just begun in the city. By the 24th he declared prematurely that "the revolution has achieved a complete victory". In the early days of the upheaval he obtained a pistol and manned the barricade blocking Friedrichstraße from Taubenstraße, but never participated in actual fighting. Virchow found his greatest political resonance not in revolutionary agitation but in the more sedate "medical reform" movement, in which physicians capitalized on the charged environment of 1848–9 to advance their most ambitious claims for professional improvement in the nineteenth century. For a year, the journal that Virchow co-founded, entitled *Die medicinische Reform*, publicized not only the activities of physicians throughout Germany and Europe, but also the contributions that put Virchow at the vanguard of the medical reform movement.[44]

The image of a pistol-wielding physician may seem incongruous, but Virchow's activities in the revolution took place against the backdrop of an increasing politicization of the medical profession. Virchow shared the distinction of having fought at the barricades with Dr Paul Boerner, who later edited the influential *German Medical Weekly*. In 1848, thirteen physicians, including the future socialist Johann Jacoby, gained seats in the Prussian National Assembly, a body to which Virchow was also elected, but from which he was disqualified for being too young.[45] Inclinations towards political activism infected entire organizations. The General Assembly of Berlin Doctors was formed on 2 April 1848 to pursue matters of professional interest, but inevitably succumbed to an atmosphere in which "the flurry of political events, the elections, the feverish excitement in Berlin pushed special interests into the background".[46] Energized by its younger and more politicized members – Virchow, for example, was the assembly's vice-president – the organization illustrated a new trend in doctors' professional representation, away from specialized and largely apolitical societies such as the Association for Scientific Medicine (itself founded only in 1844), and towards an organizational form expressing physicians' interests in explicitly political terms.[47] All over Germany – in Saxony, Silesia, Westphalia, Baden, Württemberg, Bavaria, East Prussia and especially in Berlin – the 1848 revolution saw the founding of medical societies whose particular professional ambitions were subsumed in the broader rhetoric of the revolution.[48] As Dr E A Steudel put it, the ideas of the medical reformers "have a connection with the general ideas of the time ... Therefore it is my sincere belief that a reform of our health care system that only concerns doctors will necessarily be insufficient".[49]

The equation between professional self-interest and the universalist discourse of 1848–9 did not strike the medical reformers as problematic. Political doctors did not believe that their particular grievances lay outside the problems of the political system at large. Rather, because they regarded themselves as especially oppressed by the current social order, doctors felt uniquely positioned to benefit from its reconstruction. As one physician put it, "in the medical profession are united the noblest achievements of which man is capable, and the most unworthy conditions which can be found".[50] The political awareness of physicians derived largely from a material and moral crisis in the profession during the mid-nineteenth century. Doctors at that time earned about as much as launderers, dressmakers, and butchers, and (as Virchow himself noted) considerably less than railroad workers. Increasing competition only heightened this material hardship. In the countryside, university-educated physicians had to contend with quacks and "natural healers", while in the city, which absorbed most of the 37 per cent increase in the number of doctors from 1825 to 1840, intra-professional competition centred on the limited market of patients sophisticated enough to consult trained physicians.[51] Add to this the pathetic reputation of medical science itself, plus the resentment of untrained interlopers that this entailed,[52] and the circumstances become ripe for a bid among doctors to use politics to ameliorate their collective condition.

The medical reformers – with Virchow usually at their forefront – saw a solution in the liberal politics of the revolution. In its campaign for liberty and against a repressive state, liberalism offered an emancipation from meddlesome restrictions that hampered professional freedom and its natural concomitant, material prosperity. The first objective of the reformers was therefore to abolish anachronistic holdovers in the regulation of the medical profession in Germany. The use of Latin, the absence of an all-German pharmacopoeia, and (in Bavaria) the right of communities to veto the marriages of their community doctors[53] were just a few of the most superficial legacies of an outdated organization of medicine that had continued into the mid-nineteenth century. More substantially, the state interfered in physicians' lives by subjecting them to the same type of police surveillance with which it governed many other segments of society. A certain Dr Riedel wrote an article for *Die medicinische Reform* complaining that one night he had been awakened by a patient whose ailment the doctor judged to be minor. When he bade the patient to come back later, Riedel suffered a "very energetic reprimand" from the local police officer, who enjoined him to fulfil his medical duties according to state regulations. Riedel's protest against the "policed enslavement" of the medical profession was one instance of a general resentment among doctors against state interference in their activities.[54]

Another type of interference took the form of the regulations and edicts that perpetuated a peculiar division of the medical profession into different spheres of practice. Each German state had its own scheme for classifying different types of healers. Württemberg, for example, distinguished among ten different classes of physicians. The Prussian government, acting on its own initiative in 1825, reduced the number of categories from seven to three, but maintained what the medical reformers regarded as an artificial distinction between "graduated" (university-trained) doctors, practicing mainly internal medicine, and two types of surgeons, who were substantially less educated.[55] In addition to upholding the indivisibility of medicine on scientific grounds, doctors demanded an all-encompassing and united medical profession for economic and political reasons. Obtaining permission to practise more than one type of healing – adding surgery and midwifery to internal medicine, for example – permitted doctors to cope more flexibly with increased competition.[56] A unified profession would also put physicians in a better bargaining position with the state, allowing the best trained and most prestigious doctors to assert their influence over branches of medicine from which they had been legally excluded before.[57]

The demand by doctors that the state bow out of meddlesome restrictions could sometimes take on strange twists, as evidenced by their attitudes towards quackery. Though not completely united on this issue, the great majority of medical reformers advocated that regulations outlawing quackery be abolished, thus foregoing the protection offered by the state in regulating medical practice. One explanation for this counterintuitive position was that quackery laws simply did not work. Dr F Loffler regarded current legal protections against charlatanism as weakly enforced and "illusory", likening the belief that the state could stamp out all instances of quackery to the idea that doctors could cure every patient.[58] Virchow's more explicitly liberal argument represented the dominant strain of opinion. He advocated the abrogation of quackery laws as a logical consequence of the economic freedoms of the modern world, maintaining that education of the people and the scientific progress of medicine would naturally lead patients to become sufficiently discriminating in their choice of healers. The medicalization of the population demanded that state regulations fall away as the issue of quackery ceased being a legal matter and became a "purely cultural question".[59]

Having freed doctors from the shackles of state regulation, it would be necessary to update the structure of the profession and modernize its organization. In an atmosphere of professional deregulation, doctors would assert the right to police themselves within a legal framework that substituted the liberal demand for economic and trade freedom for the guild-like organization of society. Proposals varied about the best way to accomplish this goal. On the conservative side, some suggested state-sanctioned corporations that would forcibly include all doctors in a given community. Many added provisions for disciplinary councils (*Ehrengerichte*) through which physicians could stamp out malpractice in their midst and (in some formulations) take over the state's role in disciplining the "natural healers" and other non-physician quacks who threatened mainstream practitioners.[60] Liberal physicians, with greater confidence in self-regulation, advocated independent associations with voluntary membership.[61] The majority of doctors in fact supported the free association, a proposal that found favour in the Berlin, Merseburg, Anhalt, Silesian and Saxon assemblies (although the Merseburg and Saxon assemblies advocated a hybrid, state-sanctioned free association, which they believed none the less addressed the need for "self-government of doctors").[62] Dr Robert Remak maintained that anything less than a free association would represent "the most vexatious despotism", while the psychiatrist Rudolf Leubuscher, co-editor of *Die medicinische Reform* with Virchow until 1 January 1849, believed that only through the association could the medical community truly come to regard itself as a "profession".[63]

Again, Virchow's position captured the liberal argument on the institutions of the medical profession. Like many other liberals, he regarded the free association as the "idea of our time" and as a general model for social organization. In the context of medical reform, he believed that it represented a happy medium between interference in the lives of doctors and unrestricted competition:

Free competition within the association: this is our professional freedom. Free competition outside the association leads to general charlatanism ... Association without free competition is the enslavement of the individual by the mass.[64]

Indeed, the association was to Virchow the guarantor of professional elevation. It would not only represent the political interests of doctors, but also provide material support to needy physicians. Virchow's endorsement of this liberal institution grew out of the necessity of overcoming the "material cares and degradation" through the creation of associations "guaranteeing freedom, capacity for development, and mutual rights and equality".[65]

From medical reform to liberal social science

The association was for Virchow the centrepiece of a general professional improvement based on liberal principles. But in articulating the reasons behind their espousal of liberalism, Virchow and the other medical reformers did not focus solely on their own socio-economic elevation. The medical reform movement was always one of ideas and idealism, not mere special interest politics. Virchow is the clearest example of this. He explained that "I am now no longer a half man but a whole man ... my medical credo is absorbed in my political and social credo". He regarded medical reform as but one "link in a great social reform", which also embraced freedom of speech, press and assembly; separation of Church and State; democratic, constitutional and representative government; popular education; and a hope that every individual would "respect the law ... and develop according to the gifts that nature has bestowed upon him".[66]

Other doctors also embraced liberalism as a general political credo. Of fifty-five physicians chosen to represent the Charité in Berlin medical assemblies, forty-seven identified themselves as "democrats". In the Prussian House of Representatives (1849), which included many physicians, Virchow noted that "not a single doctor subscribed to the programme of the right". He added that doctors' social conscience frequently put them "at the head of the [revolutionary] movement".[67] For Virchow, these facts proved the salutary influence of the medical profession, but in order to justify their demands for a liberalization of the profession it was necessary for the medical reformers to demonstrate a clearer connection to the universalist aims of the revolution than their personal support of liberal values suggested. To varying degrees, the medical reformers believed that their potential represented the potential of society, and that their occupation should therefore serve in some capacity as the sponsor of social improvement. To use the terms set forth in the introduction, they styled their profession a reformist élite whose occupational liberation would be conducive to the common good.

At the very least this meant explaining why doctors would perform their traditional healing role better in a liberal society. The Berlin General Assembly drafted a programme of health care reform, claiming the social benefits of an empowered profession. During the revolution, the draft noted, "the principle of public health care has become ever clearer and sharper . . . We have gradually moved from the particular interests of the profession to the universal interests of the people. The goal of our discussions has been the modern and democratic organization of public health [in Germany]". The draft made it clear, however, that the prerequisite to a public health improvement in the "universal interest" was a thoroughgoing professional reform. As "preliminary matters for decision" the assembly identified precisely those "particular interests" of the medical community that were discussed above.[68] Drafts from medical assemblies in Merseburg, Anhalt, Dresden and Silesia (to take just a few examples) similarly conflate social/ health politics with medical/professional reform.[69]

Other attempts to cast physicians as a reformist élite were more ambitious, extending the sphere of doctors' competence for sponsoring "reform" beyond their traditional role in the individual doctor-patient relationship, and placing them nearer the centre of actual political power. Salomon Neumann, a Berlin physician and Virchow's good friend, wrote in 1847 that "medical science is in its essence and marrow a social science", directly anticipating the perspective Virchow himself soon developed. By this Neumann meant that physicians should expand their usual activities to include the collection of social statistics and thereby contribute to the reorientation of politics towards the social question. In this endeavour they would enjoy access to state institutions, which had a natural and necessary responsibility to improve the people's health. Since health was the sole "property" of the poor, Neumann argued, the state must embrace social policies to protect the property rights of its citizens.[70] Leubuscher also called medicine a "purely social science" and tried to give some "practical content" to this concept. In particular, he advocated the "participation of the [state] medical administration in the worker question" through the regulation of working hours, minimum working age, and general working conditions.[71]

Neumann and Leubuscher antedated Virchow in connecting medical doctors to social politics through the model they provided for social-scientific reform. Virchow, however, wished to give the physician-élite its most far-reaching powers. In the very first issue of *Die medicinische Reform* he declared that "doctors are the natural advocates of the poor and the social question falls to a large extent within their jurisdiction".[72] In his most famous utterance of the period, Virchow extended the ideas of Neumann and Leubuscher when he declared that "medicine is a social science, and *politics is nothing more than medicine on a grand scale*".[73] In its most conservative interpretation, this statement merely reflected the principal lesson from Upper Silesia: that the political system had an obligation to implement the prescriptions of reformist physicians on a societal level in determining and eradicating the social cofactors of disease and destitution.

More provocatively, however, Virchow verged on advocating a benevolent dictatorship of the physician-élite. Politics simply was medicine on a grand scale, in this conception. Virchow envisioned a progression in German political life from "dynastic and territorial" politics up through "national democratic politics", and ultimately to a final stage of "scientific politics", which represented the most "cosmopolitan point of view", and in which the "laws of nature alone determine [our] actions".[74] A corollary to this view was that social disturbances were simply pathologies in the body politic, an outlook quite congenial to Virchow, the founder of modern pathology. The logical culmination of the Silesian idea was, after all, that diseases are "always traceable to defects in society" and that a physically unhealthy society suffered from a politically pathological constitution. Epidemics are simply "large warning signs from which the statesman can clearly read that a disturbance has occurred in the course of his people's development".[75] Society was the diseased organism, the doctor-statesman its healer, and the state the instrument through which he effected his cure.

This view of medical politics in fact anchored the legitimacy of the state to its ability to implement the doctor-statesman's cure. To Virchow, since the state "represents the moral unity" of a group, "when the state allows its citizens to be brought into a position in which they must starve to death, it ceases legally to be a state". Under the leadership of the physician-élite, it was the "duty" of government to "penetrate all parts of the state with a true, real and living spirit", claiming "any sacrifice" if necessary to cement a "solidarity of obligation" among its citizens in order to administer the medical reformers' social remedies.[76]

This strikingly sinister invocation of state power in a man known for his libertarian inclinations reflects the need to transmit medical knowledge through the organs of government authority. But the ineluctable involvement of the state in medical politics was rooted more in the requirements of liberal social science than those of a scientist dictatorship. Virchow made it clear that the metaphor of "medicine on a grand scale" was intended for distinctly liberal purposes. Medical science, to Virchow, did not seek dictatorship; if anything, scientific progress assumed a democratic exchange of ideas. A state modelled on this scientific value therefore enshrined freedom above all other principles. The social organism did not exact totalitarian claims from its constituent cells, because it was not truly an organism anyway. Virchow deflated fashionable romantic conceptions of the state with hard-nosed materialism when he wrote that "the state is certainly not and never will be an organism but a complex of organisms". Thus, "the so-called state organism therefore prospers best when individual development is most guaranteed".[77] Finally, the "pathological society" that Virchow mentioned may strike contemporary readers of Foucault as a diabolical pretext for the eradication of undesirable (pathological) social elements in an attempt to re-establish normality (the opposite of pathology). Virchow, however, did not subscribe to this sort of dualistic thinking. To him, a social "pathology" merely indicated the locus for benevolent intervention restoring diseased elements to their naturally healthy state:

We consider disease not as something personal and special but only a manifestation of life under modified conditions operating according to the same laws as apply to the living body at all times ... Every widespread disease in the nation, be it mental or physical, therefore shows us the life of the population under abnormal conditions and all we need to do is to recognize this abnormality and signal it to the statesman so he can dispose of it.[78]

In renouncing a medical politics centred on a scientist dictatorship, Virchow articulated how medicine could best take its place in the administration of the liberal state. Despite the radicalism of his claims for physicians and state power, what Virchow envisioned in their relationship was simply a fruitful cooperation between independently constituted organs of power.[79] Having advocated the free association as the vehicle for professional consolidation, Virchow outlined the terms of its position in a liberal government: "the position that physicians will occupy in the future in relation to the state will essentially depend on the attitude that the state will assume with regard to physicians. As long as states continue to exist it will be their duty to manage public health." In fulfilment of this duty, Virchow continued, the state had to match the "claims" of the individual in matters of public health with the capabilities of the medical profession.[80]

The ideal liberal partnership between the government and doctors is clearest in Virchow's remarks on the charity physicians, a group of doctors traditionally obligated to render services to non-paying patients. Jurisdiction over charity physicians fell not to the state government, but rather to local government, whose dedication to an efficient administration of health care for the poor was often suspect. Virchow deplored in particular the common practice by which the poor were forcibly matched with certain doctors, thereby eliminating any sort of choice between physician and patient. He appealed to the necessity of a freely given trust between doctor and patient, and to the natural right that a patient had to determine the treatment of his own person, as compelling arguments for a reform of the system of charity health care. This was especially necessary in light of the great social impact of the charity physician; following Neumann, Virchow emphasized that medical intervention in the lives of the poor was the surest and most concrete application of a truly social medicine and therefore the fulcrum of medical politics. He argued that as a result of the inadequate system of charity health care, epidemic diseases and general poverty had increased, and therefore that medical care must be provided to "free the poor from their extraordinary position". To improve the current system, Virchow advocated the formation of associations of doctors to provide charity work, associations whose structure would resemble the free associations he favoured for representing the profession as a whole. He specified that such associations of charity physicians could contract with local communities for fee-for-service compensation, and therefore provide a large pool of steadily and decently paid doctors from which poor patients could choose their favourite.[81] In this plan, Virchow articulated the mechanisms that mediated between associations of doctors, local government, and needy patients; he therefore satisfied the criteria he had himself set forth regarding the participation of the profession in matters of government.

Delineating a partnership between state and profession was less successful on a higher level of government. The most fundamental demand of Virchow and the other medical reformers was the convention of a special congress to debate and draft changes in the medical constitutions (*Medizinalverfassungen*) of the various German states in an attempt to solidify the various and specific aspects of medical reform. Demands for a medical congress, along with those for a national public health office and an academy of medicine,[82] demonstrated that the medical reformers did not want merely the resolution of this or that grievance, but an institutionalized partnership with the state in the formulation of medical legislation. Such concrete legislation was necessary to prevent the "arbitrariness" with which medical affairs had been administered up to that time, but proposals for a congress also made it clear that its purpose was to "involve itself in the defence of the health of citizens" and therefore that it "had a special bearing on the social question".[83] Throughout the rest of 1848 and into 1849, various assemblies made repeated requests of Prussian officials to convene a congress to draft a medical constitution, but specifics on its competence were never forthcoming. The medical reformers never agreed on whether the recommendations of the congress would be legally binding, whether they would be subject to a parliamentary vote, or whether the congress would have merely consultative powers. Virchow vacillated on this issue in advocating a "free congress, neither patronizing nor patronized" in its relations with the state. In any case, he added, it was necessary to answer "the general question concerning the proper way the democratic state should recognize [medical] legislation" prepared by "free" institutions such as the medical congress.[84]

The main reason that the issues of competence never proceeded beyond this abstract level was that negotiations never reached that stage with the state authorities. The questions of competence raised by the empowerment of a medical consultative body in a liberal-democratic state simply did not matter when such a state did not yet exist. Instead there was an illiberal bureaucracy with little concern for such questions. The Minister of Culture, to whom proposals for a medical congress were sent, repeatedly tried to steer discussions away from such questions and into more specific and less far-reaching demands of the medical community.[85] Doctors' concerns to establish the competence of a medical congress for the purpose of drafting legislation simply fell on deaf ears in a state that the revolution had failed to recast along liberal lines.

The decline of the medical reform movement

To speak of a decline in the medical reform movement is in a sense splitting hairs, because from its inception the movement never enjoyed that much popularity anyway. None the less the spirit that had animated the early meetings of the Berlin General Assembly and the first issues of *Die medicinische Reform* in spring 1848 was noticeably missing by early 1849. The earliest symptom of this was internal dissension. Though the first meetings of the assembly had attracted up to 300 doctors, or two-thirds of the medical practitioners in the capital,[86] the organization was plagued by frequent turnover in leadership and controversy over the admission of surgeons, who, it will be recalled, were not on a legal par with licensed internists. At Virchow's insistence the assembly ultimately voted to include both classes of surgeons on 11 August 1848,[87] but not before a smaller, rival organization, the Association of Doctors and Surgeons, had succeeded in stealing some of the assembly's momentum. The pages of *Die medicinische Reform* in early 1849 reveal increasing difficulties in attracting committed adherents to the movement and staving off demoralization as the reaction against the revolution set in. On 1 January 1849, Leubuscher resigned as co-editor of the journal (though he continued to contribute articles), leaving Virchow in sole charge. Six months after its first number, Virchow noted, the "powerful forces" of the counter-revolution were threatening the "rational development of our societal conditions and necessary reform of public health that goes along with this".[88]

This diagnosis was confirmed on 16 March 1849, when the General Assembly received a decisive rebuff from the Prussian Minister of Culture, to whom it had directed its proposal for a medical congress on 26 February. In polite bureaucratic language, the Minister's deputy expressed his appreciation for the assembly's proposal and that he would take it under consideration, but added that he could not give them any definite reply at that time.[89] This merely confirmed what everyone knew, which was that the Prussian State was not about to bow to the demands of a group of radical doctors. A weakened General Assembly continued for several weeks to hold out in the faint hope that the government would convene the congress, but Virchow's pronouncements on the subject reveal a distinct tone of resignation.[90] Still, he determined to go down with the ship. On 23 March 1849 he succeeded to the presidency of the assembly, but that same day saw a lively debate on whether the "weakly attended" meeting should dissolve itself completely.[91] In June Virchow published an article symbolically "handing over" the "dreams" of medical reform to a "younger generation of doctors, who still have a future, who believe in culture and its realization".[92]

On 29 June, *Die medicinische Reform* published its fifty-second and final number, signalling the end of medical reform (at least in Berlin) as an oppositional political movement directed against the Prussian government. Virchow had been drummed out of his apartment next to the Charité on 1 May, and faced suspension from his post at the hospital. Fortunately, he had accepted an appointment in Würzburg, Bavaria, that allowed him to continue his medical and scientific activities on the condition that he not make his position "a playground for radical tendencies". Considering that many of his comrades in the medical reform movement faced jail sentences, this stipulation seems quite mild. Virchow's Würzburg years witnessed his most intense scientific activity, including the formulation of his principles of pathological anatomy. Politically, however, he had been silenced, as he pragmatically accepted the necessity of replacing his democratic agitation with a dedication to the "inner life [of] the family" and the "silent achievements of daily work".[93] Only in 1859, with his election to the Berlin city council, would he rejoin political life.

The collapse of the medical reform movement grew out of its inability to marshal any sort of popular resonance in support of its cause. Just five months into the revolution, at the end of July 1848, Leubuscher bemoaned that "our infinitely rich and beautiful task, to participate in the unfolding history of a society in formation", had dissolved into debates on "trivialites".[94] Virchow attributed this floundering to the failure of a truly revolutionary upheaval to lend backbone to the movement, complaining that "the mass of the people, whose sacrifices we have requested, did not rise to the occasion".[95] In reality, however, the medical reformers had never sought such sacrifices. As Erwin Ackerknecht writes, the medical reformers never bothered to consult their "patients" and therefore failed to engage mass support for their cause; medical reform purported to represent the "general interest" without in itself being "general".[96] Virchow himself regarded an unpreparedness on the part of liberals and a consequent failure to organize as being the decisive factors in depriving the movement of a wider backing.[97]

To argue, however, that the medical reformers – like other liberal revolutionaries of 1848 – failed from a lack of social base, is to belabour the obvious. The deeper reason for their failure lies in the predicament of the liberal social scientist. The medical reformers' concern for ensuring the firm but peaceful establishment of liberal social principles in fact prevented them from relying on the very society they were trying to uplift. Virchow followed liberal thinking in his distrust of the "rabble" (*Pöbel*), which "all too often lacks judgement and education", and whose existence precluded "peace and order". To solve the social question required the "annihilation" of the rabble, by "taking it into society", thereby "letting it take part in the civil, legal and familial rights and pleasures" forming the bases of political stability. But in order to "grant [the people] a free development according to their needs", it was necessary for them to have a firm tutelary guidance.[98]

By concentrating so heavily on professional reforms as the substance of a broader social regeneration, Virchow and his colleagues betrayed their reliance on an activist élite who would carry this burden of leadership. The need for nonsubversive politics demanded a top-down approach to the social question, and this in turn required a political context favourable to the implementation of their programmes. The medical reformers did not like the state in its current incarnation, but they recognized its importance. As Virchow put it, "the current political climate is inappropriate" for medical reform "because it fails to nurture action and principle. These must be regarded as a precondition for the preparation [of medical reforms]".[99] In the absence of a political climate that could have provided either the social resonance or the state structure in which to seriously discuss and implement reforms, Virchow and his contemporaries played out a fantasy in the realm of ideas. Virchow always ended up drawing in the state, but in an era in which the state remained to him a backward and oppressive entity, he never got around to articulating the conditions of collaboration between social reformers and political authority. The decline of the medical reform movement demonstrates just how much Virchow and his colleagues operated in an isolated world of political dreams instead of realistic proposals, and thus his aspirations were ultimately consigned to irrelevance.

In the final issue of *Die medicinische Reform*, Virchow explained how the pragmatism he would adopt in Würzburg resulted not merely from his political disappointments, but also from the realization that future attempts at health reform must be grounded in a practical political context. Rather than continue a quixotic campaign, Virchow would devote himself to the concrete achievements that his participation in the 1848 revolution had failed to provide:

We can only continue to recognize the task of bringing before the people the questions of public health, the questions of daily bread and a healthy existence . . . The medical reform that we had in mind was a reform of science and of society. We have developed its principles; they will carry on without the continued existence of this journal . . . We are not abandoning the issue, merely the context.[100]

The next two chapters will deal with Virchow's attempts to re-enter politics with more realistic aspirations, first in his activities in sanitary reform in Berlin, and then in his frustrated attempts at national health care reform.

Chapter 3

Virchow and the Canalization of Berlin:
The Promise of Urban Liberalism

The sewage problem in the context of urban liberalism

In 1872 the famous English sanitary reformer Edwin Chadwick described
Berlin as the foulest-smelling capital city in Europe, and remarked that one
could recognize a Berliner by the smell of his clothing. Since the beginning
of the nineteenth century, Berlin had in fact been suffering from the
inadequacy of its sewer system, which was directly responsible for the state
of affairs that Chadwick described. Before it acquired a modern system of
drains, sewer pipes and treatment centres in the last quarter of the century,
Berlin relied on an army of workers who carted human waste away from
residences and usually emptied it into the Spree river at night. The alternative
to this was simply to leave the sewage in leaky dung pits for much less
frequent and regular cleaning. In Berlin, "ladies of night-work" referred
not to prostitutes but to women who piled buckets of excrement into open
wagons that would be dragged through the streets, leaving behind a foul
odour which wafted up to the apartments of Berlin's inhabitants. At eleven
at night, when the stench became overbearing, the Berliners closed their
windows.[101]

To handle other kinds of solid and liquid waste – runoffs after rain or
snowstorms, factory discharges, kitchen slops – Berlin had a network of
gutters that ran along the sides of roads. It was not uncommon to find
human waste contaminating these open troughs. As Berlin became more
densely populated and its wastewater production increased, the gutters had
to be widened and deepened to such an extent that they became a health
hazard for those pedestrians whose feet accidentally slipped into the muck.
In order to avoid this sort of occurrence, many residents wore boots even
in the summer. The city did have a primitive system of canals as well as
underground pipes to collect the gutter waste and eventually channel it into
the Spree, but this system was hardly comprehensive. The water that did
make it into the river polluted it, of course, a problem further complicated
by the slow movement of the Spree's waters.

Between the early 1870s, when the sewage problem reached its peak, and
the 1890s, Berlin underwent a radical change. Beginning in 1873 and

extending over the next twenty-one years, the city instituted a "canalization" system that offered a solution to the twin problems of human waste disposal and drainage of incidental and runoff waters. At the same time, the system avoided a contamination of the Spree. The project proved extremely successful. Having solved its sewage problem later than many other European cities – London, Paris, Hamburg and Frankfurt, for example – Berlin had the luxury of drawing on their experience, and thus implemented what became a model system whose fame spread beyond Europe. A E Silk, a British engineer working in Calcutta (whose sanitary problems surely rivalled Berlin's), wrote a report suggesting that Berlin's system might favourably be applied to his city. His conclusion, utterly typical of contemporary accounts of Berlin's canalization, deserves quotation:

As a city, Berlin can be placed in the first rank of capital cities of the world ... The cleanliness of the streets and the absence of all bad smells in the city are ample proofs of the wise and liberal policy adopted by the City Council in the management of sanitary affairs.[102]

This was a far cry from Chadwick's damning pronouncement.

In the hagiography of the Berlin sewer system, Virchow's name ranks higher than any other. Isidor Kastan, in his reminiscences of nineteenth-century Berlin, praised the "great researcher and man of the people" for his "dogged and persistent dedication to this highly regarded project" through which he overcame "all the resistance and spiteful attacks" from the opponents of the system.[103] To a great extent this reputation is deserved. Through his scientific expert opinions, as well as his political leadership in the Berlin city council, Virchow played the pivotal role in the city's canalization. The word "pivotal" is especially appropriate here, because characteristically Virchow served as the bridge between the political and scientific aspects of the sewerage campaign. He regarded the project as a practical application of medical politics, in that it joined detailed technical researches with the community's responsibility to provide a clean and healthy environment for its residents. Virchow himself thus donned the cap of physician-reformer in his sanitary improvement activity, and collaborated with other urban élites – city councilmen, engineers, scientists – in order to clean up the city.

Virchow's success owed less to his personal leadership than to the context in which he operated, however. In the logic of liberal social science, he depended on a state, in the form of the Berlin municipal government. His consistent reliance on the city government will become clear first of all in his late appearance in the canalization story – the way had been prepared for him before he entered the picture – and also in the literal sense that the city employed him to investigate sewerage reform. Most importantly,

Virchow's campaign for sanitary reform took place at a time when city governments in Germany were flexing their political muscle. Liberals in particular were able to dominate urban politics even while their aspirations on the national stage seemed shaky at best.[104] Attracted by traditions of local self-government that had been legally enshrined by the so-called Stein reforms of 1808, liberals of various stripes took refuge in the city.[105] Urban liberalism was thus a condominium embracing different colours of political opinion, in which Virchow happily played a large part but – as this chapter will also suggest – he adjusted his politics to conform to the aspirations of the movement as a whole. Civic leaders upheld the liberal ideal of rational self-government, which allowed them to claim that their urban autonomy represented a beacon of progress in an otherwise backward and meddlesome Prussian State. The canalization campaign fought by Virchow and other sanitary reformers, characterized by a "fierceness seldom found in such a technical matter",[106] thus lent political meaning to an ostensibly apolitical undertaking. Urban liberals sought to prove that their government was the better government, and to win esteem both for their cities and their political philosophy.

To legitimate this contention, liberals sought to improve their cities through beautification and development projects, but the critical test of liberal city government lay in its handling of economic and demographic growth.[107] As the increase in size and complexity of city life began to present problems demanding a social solution, city governments were in fact forced to undertake projects in housing reform, poor relief and sanitation. Sanitation reform turned out to be the urban social reformers' most successful accomplishment and, as the largest city in Prussia, Berlin was most in need of improvement in this area. Between the years 1822 and 1871 the population of Berlin nearly quadrupled, and by 1880 the city counted over a million inhabitants. The old system of channeling waste by whatever method into the Spree was increasingly intolerable; Virchow reckoned that if all of Berlin's liquid human waste reached the river, 1.04 billion cubic centimetres would have been emptied into the waterway daily.[108] Crying out for a radical remedy, this situation presented urban liberals, and in particular those in Berlin, with a tremendous opportunity to remake the city and enhance civic pride. Canalization represents their attempt to convert the liabilities of demographic explosion into a political vindication of liberal self-government.

This road was fraught with challenges, however, because the unprecedented magnitude of urban problems such as sanitation demanded an equally extraordinary response from city administrators. The responsibilities of city government remained the same – education, public works, fire protection, poor relief, waterworks, and of course sewerage – but the approach to these responsibilities became qualitatively different. In problems like sanitation, city governments enlisted the aid of engineers and scientists whose expertise was needed to design and implement projects, like canalization, on an extraordinary scale. Some viewed the elevation of technical and scientific knowledge to prime determinant of public policy as an inappropriate leap of faith, given the magnitude of the projects that such knowledge informed. This qualm had to be overcome. A second concomitant of the extension of government responsibility was an administrative and bureaucratic reorganization that challenged the social bases of urban liberalism. Specifically, government expansion transformed traditional networks of governing notables, who knew one another and who participated in government in an amateur capacity, into to a more diffuse governing class, spread out over a larger city. At the same time it demanded a more professional commitment on the part of urban politicians and the hiring of outside experts and advisers.[109] While the social character of city government remained homogeneously bourgeois,[110] the spirit that had knit it together seemed in danger. Berlin's Magistrat, the administrative council standing just over the city council, remarked that the multiplication of administrative posts and a sprawling governmental apparatus led to a situation that no longer reflected the "civic communal spirit" originally inspired by the Stein reforms.[111] What was needed in the modern age was a redefinition of civic spirit that addressed pressing governmental responsibilities while preserving the tradition of self-government that Stein had institutionalized.

The challenges posed by urban growth and the qualitative and quantitative expansion of city government did not end there for Berlin. Being a capital city, Berlin was subject to two governments – Prussian and local – both of which claimed extensive influence over the resolution of the sewage problem. The Magistrat remarked that the interference of the king and his government in the administration of Berlin had stunted the growth of confident self-government. Only in the 1840s, according to the Magistrat, did the city begin to see itself "not merely as the residence of the king, but also as the property of its citizens".[112] Given the relative immaturity of self-government in Berlin, jurisdictional struggles between various Prussian ministries and the municipal government decisively influenced the history of the city's canalization. Thus, urban liberals faced three challenges in the construction of a sewer system for Berlin. In addition to mustering political support for Virchow's claim that sanitation was an integral part of medical politics and the responsibility of the state (in its municipal incarnation), the proponents of canalization had also to provide a technically, scientifically and administratively feasible solution to a qualitatively unprecedented sanitation problem, as well as to claim the project as their own. The attempt by Berlin's city government to parlay these challenges into political opportunity will be the subject of the following pages.

Ineffective solutions from state and local governments

The first initiatives taken to solve the sewage problem in Berlin actually came from the Prussian government, not the municipal authorities. In 1842 the government commissioned expert opinions from August Crelle and Joseph Baeyer to suggest possible ways of cleaning up the capital, and while these produced few practical results, they reiterated in stark terms the necessity of a regular flushing and cleaning of the street gutters. By this time, the newly crowned King Frederick William IV had taken a personal interest in the sewage question, and in 1852 he began negotiations with two English entrepreneurs, Charles Fox and Thomas Crampton, who proposed to construct a comprehensive water-supply system for Berlin (which up to that time had relied solely upon springs and wells). Such a system would satisfy the increasing drinking water needs of the town, but its main objective was to allow for a systematic and thorough cleaning of the gutters.[113] Soon the king decided to turn over responsibility for negotiations to the police department, which, importantly, was an organ of the Prussian government. The state government had tried to involve the city in the financing of the waterworks, but, heavily compromised by its recent expenditures on gas and lighting improvements, the city declined the offer.[114] Thus it was without the cooperation of the city that, in 1852, police chief Hinckeldey concluded a contract with the English Waterworks Company, led by Fox and Crampton and financed privately as a limited-liability corporation. The waterworks began operation in 1856.

The waterworks did not solve the sewage problem. Following the letter of its contract, the English company declined to provide sufficient water to clean the entire city. High-handed bureaucratic attempts by Hinckeldey and his successor, von Bernuth, to circumvent the company's contracts and force it to provide more water proved ineffective.[115] Even where the city was well-provided, the added water use actually increased the amount of sewage being produced in Berlin. Responding to these deficiencies, the state government again intervened.[116] In 1860, Prussian Minister for Trade, Commerce, and Public Works von der Heydt commissioned Eduard Wiebe to lead a fact-finding mission to such cities as London, Paris, Cologne and Hamburg to study their sewer systems and suggest more comprehensive solutions for Berlin. Wiebe's proposal, published in 1861, defined the political debate on canalization for roughly the next decade. Briefly put, the proposal recommended replacing the system of dung pits, cart-removal, and side gutters with a network of underground sewers that would collect both runoff waters from the streets as well as human waste from water-closets (to be constructed). These various waters would be gathered at a point northwest of the city, somewhere between Charlottenburg and Spandau, where they would be dumped into the river. To be constructed over twenty-two years, the canalization system would cost 13 million marks to build and about 90,000 marks a year to operate.[117]

The primary political effect of Wiebe's publication was to provide a focus for debate about which the various interests could situate themselves. The most fervent opponents of Wiebe's plan were the big agriculturalists, who saw in the current system of cart-removal the opportunity to obtain valuable fertilizer, in the form of human waste, at low cost for their estates.[118] Diluting this waste with street runoffs in the sewers, and then disposing of the whole mess into the Spree, deprived agriculture of this resource. In 1862, the famous agricultural chemist Justus von Liebig articulated the scientific rationalization behind this view. Liebig not only argued for the beneficial and indeed unrivalled quality of human waste as fertilizer, but also warned forebodingly of the consequences of neglecting this resource. Essentially, Liebig saw in agriculture the foundation of a nation's economy, and suggested that if Germany failed to capitalize on its endowments in this area, it would be consigned to an ever-shrinking role in world affairs. Claiming for his ideas a provenance dating back to Adam Smith, Liebig sought to steer the political economy in a more scientific direction by presenting his investigations into agricultural chemistry as the determinants of an agronomically-oriented philosophy.[119] In 1872 Liebig declared that since human waste had a value "beyond all description", the canalization of Berlin would represent a "calamity" of the highest order.[120]

Another group opposed to Wiebe's project represented not the concerns of the countryside, but rather those of the city, and objected to the technical complexities and questionable public health benefits inherent in the system. For one thing, collecting all waste waters at a point northwest of Berlin posed enormous difficulties, especially in removing water all the way from the southeast section of town. And as the city expanded radially, the collection point would have to be moved further downstream, and the network of sewers would have to be extended to points farther southeast. Furthermore, even if the English Waterworks Company could be prevailed upon to increase its supply of water, the channeled sewage might not be diluted sufficiently to render it harmless. Releasing this water into the Spree therefore carried dangerous potential, not only for the residents of towns downstream, but also for the inhabitants of Berlin itself. A very slow-moving river, the Spree was unsuitable for rapidly carting away the large volume of waste that would enter the sewage canals, and so some of the pollution could possibly linger in the vicinity of Berlin.[121]

The Wiebe plan crystallized debate on the question "Canalization or Cart-Removal?", but generated an extended political deadlock. In the early 1860s, the debate had not yet taken on a public character, and remained largely confined to government circles. The various arms of the Prussian government took different positions. In 1862 the Royal Technical Construction Committee expressed its support for Wiebe, followed in 1868 by the police department, which was concerned to "defend its jurisdictional interests in sanitary matters". The Agricultural Ministry, for obvious reasons, opposed Wiebe.[122] The Berlin city council, whose appointment of a commission in 1861 to investigate sewerage reform represented the municipality's first concrete initiative on the subject, was divided and irresolute. City engineer Spott was worried about potential cost overruns and the technical complexity of Wiebe's project, and he was joined by Thorwirth, who emphasized the possibility of contaminating the Spree and the agricultural opportunity costs that Liebig had pointed out. On the other side, the engineer Veitmeyer, who had travelled with Wiebe on his fact-finding mission, supported the canalization project, as did councilman von Unruh, who regarded the "necessity of canalization" as a "question of our time".[123]

The Berlin Magistrat, which by 1866 was tired of five years of foot-dragging by the municipal commission, decided to seize the initiative and came out in favour of Wiebe's plan "in principle", requesting the city council to render an opinion on the feasibility of canalization. On 17 November, the council declined to make a definitive recommendation, citing the lack of technical information on the appropriateness of Wiebe's plan and specifying a list of questions that first must be answered.[124] The council's vacillation reflected the fact that the interests grouped around Wiebe's plan were not yet mature: as long as civic-minded but skeptical supporters of sanitary reform were found in the same camp as self-interested agriculturalists, a true appraisal of interests could not be made. In an attempt to remedy the dearth of adequate information and generate new proposals, the city council took matters in hand when in February 1867 it empowered a new commission to conduct scientific investigations. Over the next five years the council granted it about 120,000 marks for expenses.[125]

Virchow's bid for a practical medical politics

Virchow was chosen to lead the commission, and his activities provided both the scientific foundation for a more sophisticated canalization plan, and gave him a springboard to tout sanitary reform as an application of medical politics. The fact that he had previously been appointed to head a separate commission by the Prussian Minister von der Heydt (in 1865)[126] demonstrates that the city's newfound commitments to finding practical solutions to canalization did not represent a simple passing of the torch from state to local government. None the less, Virchow conducted his most crucial and detailed scientific researches under the auspices of the municipal commission.

One of the first scientific imperatives was to evaluate the condition of Berlin's groundwater. Ever since the Bavarian scientist Max von Pettenkofer had first articulated his influential groundwater theory in 1854, the matter had assumed commanding importance in German public health circles.[127] According to this theory, a fall in the level of groundwater left a layer of moistened soil in which infectious diseases, like cholera, could easily flourish. It was this half-aerated, half-moistened soil that Pettenkofer regarded as most epidemically volatile.[128] As far as the canalization question was concerned, this theory had two implications. First, Virchow's commission had to decide whether canalization could possibly moderate dangerous fluctuations in groundwater by channeling off excess waters. And second, if this were not the case, there arose the reverse question: could seepage from canal pipes actually contaminate the soil by releasing harmful human excrement into it? With regard to the first issue, the extreme flatness of the Berlin countryside rendered impossible any reliance on the natural gradient of the land; pipes would have to be laid out along an artificial slope to ensure proper drainage. This meant that deep-laid sewers could theoretically serve to collect waters from shallower pipes that formed the first order of waste water drainage. These shallow pipes could be made porous to groundwater through proper selection of building materials. The pressure differential between a densely packed surrounding soil and such a drain pipe whose density was lowered by the presence of air would ensure that groundwater flowed into, and not out of, the pipes. This conclusion laid to rest both of the issues raised by the Pettenkofer theory.[129] One further logical consequence of the groundwater condition in Berlin was not spelled out by the General Report produced by Virchow's commission, but it did have practical implications for the canalization plans proposed in Berlin. Wiebe's proposal had relied on an extremely long network of sewers, which made it extremely difficult to lay out a system of deep and shallow pipes to provide a suitably steep artificial gradient. This obstacle would have to be overcome in the final canalization plan.

From a discussion of groundwater, one of the putative causes of health hazards related to the canalization question, Virchow moved to one of the alleged effects. This was the issue of mortality due to faults of municipal sanitation, and its possible connection to the inadequacies of sewerage.[130] Through statistical analysis of approximately 350,000 deaths in Berlin, Virchow and his commission concluded that general mortality in the city had increased fully 82 per cent between 1854 and 1858 and 1864 and 1868. Moreover, he noted a rise in mortality in the summer, which time also happened to correspond with an increase in the groundwater level. By whatever causal factors – he did not say how Pettenkofer's theory was involved here – it was clear to Virchow that "nothing appears more settled than the fact that water level influences mortality".[131] Upon investigating further, Virchow determined that the steep rise in mortality in the summer months was due entirely to the premature death of infants: death rates of other age categories actually declined in summer. Given that birth rates actually decreased in the summer, and given his dismissal of other alternative explanations, Virchow could not escape the conclusion that deficiencies in air, water or nutrition – in all cases "preventable conditions" – were responsible for increased infant mortality, and therefore fell within the scope of public health care. In order that his point not be lost on less perceptive readers, Virchow cited evidence connecting decreased infant mortality with the introduction of comprehensive sanitation and sewerage projects in England.[132] This scientific finding significantly furthered the cause of canalization advocates in Berlin.

Virchow did not yet regard canalization as a foregone conclusion, however. He continually emphasized that the proper aim of his scientific research was to inform public policymaking, not dictate it. As a general principle, Virchow rejected premature acceptance of any monocausal account of sanitary deficiencies – such as Pettenkofer's groundwater theory – and instead advocated a more flexible, empirical approach. For large cities especially, the factors affecting health were so complex that adopting any particular explanation was an affront to the principles of scientific objectivity.[133] In this connection, Virchow's scientific attitude towards Berlin's sanitation problems parallels the approach he took in Upper Silesia, when he stressed the social determinants of disease but maintained that climate and biology also contributed to the typhus epidemic.

The specific application of this belief lay in Virchow's rejection of the canalization/removal dichotomy. Ever since Wiebe's plan, the debate on sewerage reform had centred around the issue: should waste, particularly human waste, continue to be disposed of by a revamped and systematized cart-removal, or should sewers be constructed to solve the problem? Virchow had several reasons for opposing such a reductionist approach. For one thing, the choice of sewer system depended entirely on the particular conditions of the town or city in question.[134] Though he maintained that in general, canalization was appropriate for cities and removal for towns, the Berlin case demonstrated that other factors – the absence of a natural gradient, for instance – compelled a detailed consideration of all circumstances. But equally noteworthy, even if canalization was right for Berlin, the length of time required to construct the system meant that an orderly (and improved) removal would have to do for the interim. Therefore, "there is no system of canalization that can dispense altogether with removal".[135] To simplify the question by positing canalization as the opposite of removal acted as an impediment to scientific debate, according to Virchow's conception.

Virchow's endorsement of scientific flexibility inspired a desire to promote an active public discourse on sanitary reform. His advocacy of a democratic political process and his belief in scientific debate in fact reflected a uniform commitment to freedom and pluralism. Virchow commented that each conflict of political interests – agriculture versus public health, the taxpayer versus the government, the householder versus the police – had a viable "standard for judgement" and therefore a place in sewerage reform. Applying a dialectical perspective to the democratic process of conflict resolution, Virchow maintained that such standards would ultimately produce a "reconciliatory viewpoint" that not only revealed the will of the populace, but also could "rank among the scientific convictions of the age".[136] Writing these words in 1868, Virchow looked on the coming agitation campaign as an opportunity to effect a democratic resolution of the canalization question. By this time, the discussion of Wiebe's plan had moved outside purely governmental circles and begun to spill over into the public and local press. In surveying the political activity up to 1868, Virchow saw in the "presentation of facts skilfully and intelligently compiled" a movement afoot to divert citizens from a reform of their sewer system. Referring to the "agricultural chemists" and "political economists" who opposed canalization from agronomical and financial perspectives respectively, Virchow derided those who sought to gain political advantage by casting the false dichotomy between removal and canalization as a struggle between economic prudence and misplaced reformism.[137]

Thus convinced of the need for a more rational discourse, Virchow hastened to add his own "standard for judgement" to those being offered by the opponents of Wiebe's plan. From the discussion of his liberal conception of medical politics in 1848–9, it becomes clear that he did not regard his commitment to open dialogue in science and politics as incompatible with the firm stance that he himself would take. Here, Virchow merely applied his belief that scientific recommendations should have a benevolent, guiding role in public policy, not an overwhelming or dictatorial one. Virchow's first aim was to awaken the public to the pressing health considerations behind sewerage reform. He described the attitude of most of the populace as "indifferent" and "fatalistic", disinclined to believe that sanitary reform could alleviate the depredations of cholera and typhus.[138] Virchow clearly disagreed with this apathetic attitude, since his investigations into infant mortality and groundwater had furnished a clear locus for effective and practical intervention. Thus, without committing to the Wiebe plan in particular, Virchow maintained that a true sewer system of some sort was necessary to stabilize the groundwater, *"for we can do well financially and hygienically only by means of systematic canalization"*.[139] This statement demonstrates Virchow's belief that in the free interplay of interests, the public health should none the less assume commanding importance. At times he defended this belief on purely ethical grounds, writing at one point that health must be the "absolutely deciding factor" in public policy and that "whatever the financial consequences, they must be borne when public health demands it".[140] But he also developed a more conservative rationale that would appeal to urban sanitary reformers less convinced than he was of the inherent value of human life. That is, he added economic justifications to ethical ones. He stated that in his hierarchy of political legitimacy, "agricultural interests must take second place to municipal economic development", and that this development depended on public health, because *"state and town acquire their value only through human beings and their work ... Can there be a greater loss than the loss of human lives?"*[141] This calculated appeal was designed to demonstrate the viability of a practical medical politics, by emphasizing the broad value of his activities on the Prussian and municipal commissions. Led by his scientific findings and liberal principles, Virchow arrived at a prescription for sanitary reform that the government could apply in order to improve the health of its constituents.

Hobrecht's plan and the agitation campaign

Despite the depth of Virchow's scientific researches – his commission published thirteen volumes (and three appendices) of excruciatingly detailed findings[142] – the only canalization plan on the table as late as 1872 was Wiebe's. But in 1869, Virchow's municipal commission had taken steps to offer the city council a more feasible proposal than that which Wiebe had been able to offer. On 11 March of that year, the commission hired the engineer James Hobrecht to suggest alternatives.[143] More than a simple engineer, Hobrecht was an urban liberal reformer in the style of Virchow. He had both supervised an urban development plan for Berlin in 1861 and designed a canalization system for the city of Stettin.[144] Furthermore, Hobrecht embodied the "new man" in urban liberalism at the same time as he retained links to the old system of notables. Hired by the city council for his technical expertise, Hobrecht is a case study in the professionalization of urban politics, but his family connections – his brother, Arthur, became mayor of Berlin in 1874 – betokened the lasting importance of personal contacts. Author of the plan that would eventually be implemented in Berlin and later the director of its implementation, Hobrecht worked alongside Virchow in the canalization campaign. Their conceptions of the role of government in sanitary reform differed, however; Hobrecht's more conservative political philosophy demonstrated that urban liberalism was not a rigid ideology but a political condominium embracing and supporting many shades of opinion. Specifically, Hobrecht was more inclined than Virchow to idealize the state (or at least less inclined to specify limits upon it). He regarded good health as the "cement" of a "love and loyalty to the state" and elided bodily health with the spiritual elevation of society and dedication to the state, which he defined as a "community standing for the service of an ideal". To safeguard this ideal, therefore, it became the duty of the community to look after the health of its members, through projects like sewerage reform.[145]

Though sometimes prone to such abstract musings, Hobrecht developed an eminently practical canalization plan for Berlin.[146] His critical insight and improvement over Wiebe was to split the city into several radial districts, like pieces of a pie, and to construct the canal systems serving these districts completely independently of one another. Each sewerage network would collect all the waste waters of a particular district – mixing street water and human waste[147] – and channel them to an irrigation field outside of town, where the waste could be treated and then spread over a tract of otherwise barren land to be purchased by the city. The system had the virtues of cutting down drastically the distance waste had to be carried, because any given point would not be unacceptably far from the collection point for the district; and it allowed for almost indefinite expansion of the city. More branches could always be added to the network, and if necessary, the irrigation fields could be relocated further outside of town. Finally, Hobrecht's proposal avoided any sort of contamination of the Spree. These advantages succeeded in winning over a large number of civic-minded sceptics but could not appease the big agriculturalists. For though the city later contracted to some smallholders to farm garden-plots on the newly enriched irrigation fields, the waste would still be unavailable for transport to the large estates.[148]

The Magistrat received the plan on 1 August 1871 and placed it before the city council on 16 November of the next year, advocating the construction of Radial System III, which would drain the centre of the city and serve as a pilot project to test the feasibility of Hobrecht's system. The estimated costs of this radial system, one among eleven others for the rest of the city, would be 6 million marks – nearly half what Wiebe's entire project had envisioned. The details of financing the project were not yet clear, but funds would probably come from increases in local taxes and fees.[149] In light of the "urgency of the situation", Virchow and his municipal commission endorsed Hobrecht's proposal even though the commission's General Report had not yet been published.[150] With the technical and scientific hurdles thus cleared, the project now became the subject of city council discussion. As details of the plan began to leak to the public, the agitation campaign described by Virchow reached its most vituperative peak, and finally took on the character of a fully public debate. This was because Hobrecht's contribution finally gave competing interests the possibility of sinking their teeth into a technically mature sewer system proposal. As Virchow had hoped, political discussion began gradually to revolve around the interests of the city, so that other concerns were pushed aside.

This development is clearest in the campaign of the agriculturalists, who were naturally the first to heap scorn upon the Hobrecht scheme. In November 1872 the *German Agricultural Newspaper* ran a series of eleven articles attacking the plan, but it offered little practical objection to it besides reiterating the traditional line that agriculture needed the fertilizer and maintaining that canalization would probably not work anyway.[151] Continuing its criticisms through the winter, the newspaper saw fit to vilify Virchow as well. In February 1873 the editorship criticized Virchow's General Report from the municipal commission as "one-sided, superficial, and partisan".[152] Such fervent attacks concealed internal dissension among the agriculturalists, however. The Prussian *Annals of Agriculture* during this period maintained its contrasting portrayal of Virchow as a sensible moderate, and reported that in 1872 an organization representing estate-owners in the vicinity of Berlin had disavowed itself from the tactics of the *German Agricultural Newspaper*, which in their opinion had abandoned its "otherwise justified" opposition to canalization in favour of *ad hominem* attacks and other "unworthy means of struggle".[153] The agriculturalists, concerned primarily with their own economic interests, were on the wane by 1872–3 and they seemed to realize this.

In the meantime, initiative during the agitation campaign had passed to the residents of the city themselves. More precisely, the campaign centred around the bourgeoisie. Though a few articles appeared in more popular newspapers – mainly in favour of canalization, for tenants had little to lose in taxes to fund the project[154] – the main participants in the dialogue were landlords, pharmacists, doctors, chemists, factory owners, and other middle-class citizens. The predominance of bourgeois elements in the canalization campaign does not mean that they automatically endorsed Hobrecht's solution. In petitions addressed to the city council, embryonic citizen action committees expressed their fears that canalization would "exceed the taxpaying abilities of the population" and force landlords to raise rents dramatically to cover their costs in taxes. According to the calculations of one group, a revamped cart-removal could remove human waste at much less cost than canalization (though the group did not say what should be done with street and runoff waters). Many of these groups remained sceptical about the technical advantages of Hobrecht's plan, expressing concern that noxious gases from sewer pipes could creep up into houses and cause disease. Some cited statistical evidence from England allegedly disproving any correlation between canalization and reduced mortality.

Despite such grave reservations, however, the citizenry was agreed on two key points. First, Berlin's sanitary conditions were in need of radical improvement of some kind, whether through canalization or systematized removal. Even those who derided the "canalization fanatics" acknowledged that their catchphrase, "It cannot remain this way!", enjoyed a wide popularity. Second, the commitment to a solution by the municipality ensured that whatever its form, it would appeal to "all those citizens who are truly concerned with the well-being of the city and who, in particular, want to moderate the effects of ever more threatening epidemics".[155] In short, popular agitation provided the political will to clean up Berlin.

This popular will found expression in the city council debates of spring 1873. During March of that year, councilman Beutner spoke for the current mood in the city council and echoed Virchow's rationales for canalization when he appealed to the council's patriotism and "civic spirit" to solve what had become a "burning" question. He remarked that the sewerage problem had reached a stage where it simply had to be solved, and that the council should spare absolutely no means – "no costs, no efforts" – in order to relieve the city of its sewage blight.[156] The city council soon validated Beutner's stance, reaching an "essential decision" in favour of canalization on 3 March 1873 and then approving the construction of Hobrecht's Radial System III on 15 May of that year.[157] Hobrecht himself would oversee the building of his system.

This final decision to support Hobrecht demonstrates the willingness of the council to bow to the decision of the Magistrat despite the reservations of the populace. Owing to the structure of Berlin's municipal government, the Magistrat had decisive political leverage in important policy matters. The council in fact acted primarily in an advisory capacity, while the Magistrat both proposed legislation and reserved the right to sanction or disapprove it. Though this arrangement was undemocratic, the members of the Magistrat and city council were drawn from the same social groups and participated jointly in most important commissions (Virchow's was a "mixed" commission, for instance).[158] Berlin's Magistrat had favoured canalization ever since 1866 as a necessary guard against epidemics, because of their "close connection to the groundwater conditions".[159] In 1873 the Magistrat declared its belief that Virchow's commission had resolved by "lengthy and detailed studies of all pertinent questions" any qualms it had about Hobrecht's proposal. Trusting in Virchow's scientific findings, the Magistrat concluded, "the laity has barely any choice but to accept [Hobrecht's] plan".[160]

Virchow himself was ambivalent about the Magistrat extending such trust to nondemocratic commissions such as his own. In the Prussian parliament, he remarked that placing health policy matters like canalization in the hands of "special corporations" prevented any "narrowminded decisions" of fickle democratic majorities, but he none the less regarded giving such corporations the power to decide on "questions relating to the life and health of city residents" as a "dangerous thing".[161] In this instance, however, he was obligated to rely on a context of urban government that sought to implement public projects on its own initiative.[162] Hobrecht summed up this idea when he wrote in 1872 that he longed for a day in which political distractions such as the "terrorism" of the agriculturalists would give way to purely technical considerations in municipal decision-making on public sanitation. The result would be an enlightened leadership of the city government, in which "initiative, decision, and responsibility are always left to public authorities".[163] In the climate of urban liberalism in Berlin, popular agitation thus remained limited to providing the legitimacy for public health reform. The canalization campaign had validated Virchow's application of medical politics to sewerage improvement, but the democratic process that Virchow envisioned was only partly realized due to the zeal of the Magistrat and men like Hobrecht in pushing through their own projects.

The consolidation of municipal authority and of urban liberalism

The decision to build Radial System III did not mark the end of the process by which the city government asserted its control over municipal sanitation. In the years 1874–7 the progress of canalization involved the city in jurisdictional struggles with the Prussian government. These struggles hinged on extremely technical matters, but viewed from a historical perspective, they signal the consolidation of the municipality's bid to wrest control over sanitary matters from a state whose intervention it considered both politically annoying and administratively inappropriate.

In 1874 the city began to tackle the question of how to induce homeowners to join the canalization system. From a technical and administrative standpoint it was necessary that every developed piece of land be connected.[164] In 1872 Hobrecht counted among those who believed that the rates could be structured so as to give a natural incentive to homeowners to connect their houses to the system, by making canalization cheaper than cart-removal.[165] As building progressed and expenses increased, however, it became obvious that in order to avoid huge debt, the city had to exact more from its residents. Moreover, since the new system provided new advantages over cart-removal – washing out gutters and generally addressing the "interest of the community as such" – the municipality considered it "justified" to impose higher tariffs.[166] Sewerage reform differed from most other public projects of this era – gas, electricity, waterworks – in that it would never become a profitable enterprise,[167] but rather represented one of the first incursions of the municipal government into the pocketbooks of its citizens in order to promote the general aims of the community.

As of 1874, however, the city government itself did not have the legal power to make such claims, but rather had to rely on the co-operation of the police. Virchow bemoaned this circumstance, for he regarded the police as "patriarchal" and incompetent in their attempts to govern the city. Pointing to their poor handling of the city's waterworks and their eagerness to turn over its finances to a private corporation, Virchow maintained that the right of forcing connections to this new canalization must be granted to the community itself. Only through a unified, responsible and empowered local administration would city officials best be able to represent the interests of their general constituency.[168] His hopes for a broad reform in this area were disappointed, but in this specific case the city did obtain what it needed. After lengthy negotiations with the police, municipal officials hammered out two ordinances that required landlords to connect to the system, contributing 1 per cent per year of the rental value of their properties to the canalization fund.[169] Despite their necessary reliance on the police, the municipality did succeed in preventing state meddling in the actual financing of the system. Hobrecht argued that the city alone should bear the burden of financing the system, for despite the potential generosity of state contributions, it would put the city in a "more favourable financial situation" if it could manage the costs of canalization by itself.[170] The huge loans and expenditures undertaken by the municipal government over the next twenty years demonstrated that this political and administrative control meant a lot to Berlin's officials. According to Virchow's reckoning, by 1890 the city had spent 79 million marks on Hobrecht's canalization scheme, of which 60 million had been borrowed.[171] Though costly, the decision by the city to finance sewerage reform by itself is clear evidence of its commitment to local self-government.

In other matters it was not so simple to reach an accommodation with the Prussian government. Due to the historical development of the city, many of Berlin's public squares and streets were owned not by the city but by an agency called the *Straßenfiskus* (literally, "street treasury"). There was some confusion as to what this arm of the Prussian government actually was; a puzzled Virchow labeled it a "mythical" entity. Such patchwork jurisdiction and inefficient organization led inevitably, in Virchow's opinion, to disagreements between city and state governments.[172] In fact, difficulties did arise when the city tried to extend the canalization system to those areas of Berlin owned by the state. According to Kastan, the Prussian government "did not show the slightest inclination" to remedy the "scandalous conditions in its capital" through canalization and balked at the city's desire to overstep its legal jurisdiction.[173] Kastan was only partly right; it is more accurate to say that some Prussian agencies demonstrated an interest in sewerage reform, while others dragged their heels. To the municipal government, it was this inconsistency more than anything else that proved that state government was ill-constituted to address local needs. By 1875, again after lengthy negotiations, the city acquired control over the streets of the town and was finally able to install sewers to drain them.

But only two years later another jurisdictional dispute arose. This time, the police, along with the Prussian Ministry for Trade, Commerce, and Public Works and the Royal Technical Construction Committee, objected to a special feature required in the construction of Radial Systems I and II. For technical reasons, these systems required safety outlets to channel drain waters into public canals and waterways (under government jurisdiction) in the event of heavy rainfall. Hobrecht maintained that damming devices existed to prevent the discharge of unclean sewage into the waters, but the concerned government ministries none the less asserted their right to approve or veto any construction projects that made use of the safety outlets. The city objected to such interference, and the Prussian government attempted to justify its position by citing complaints about pollution by homeowners near the waterways. By 1880, however, the complaints had died down and the matter ceased to be an issue.[174]

These tiffs reinforced the city administrators' belief that the only practical and advisable implementation of the canalization system lay in a more unrestricted administration for the local officials. They proved that the city needed to establish a uniform and rational control over all aspects of Berlin's sewer system in order to proceed with its construction and operation efficiently. Slowly but surely, Berlin's municipal government gained the control it needed. In 1872 it purchased the city's waterworks and began operating them two years later; in 1875 it took over street-cleaning services from the Prussian government (again after much struggle and negotiation); and throughout the decade it purchased land from the state and from private holders in order to establish the irrigation fields required by Hobrecht's scheme.[175] This consolidation of control vindicated a principle Virchow articulated consistently in reference to municipal sanitation. Since it was "extraordinarily difficult to establish normative [scientific] principles" for sanitation measures that addressed "the very diverse local conditions" of each city, the sphere of sanitation and sewage properly lay with the community.[176]

Fortuitously for the progress of urban liberalism, the technical necessity of respecting local conditions enhanced the political ability of the municipal authorities to assert their control over Berlin. In their dealings with the government authorities they successfully established the principle that they could do the job better than the Prussian administration. More generally, the experiences of canalization proved that the coordination of technical expertise and efficient administration was best carried out on a municipal level. After all, most of the technical and scientific research took place under Virchow's municipal commission, and the building of the system was led by Hobrecht and other city employees. Furthermore, the successful sewerage reform of Berlin by canalization not only vindicated local government *per se*, but also proved that liberal local government in particular was prepared to meet the challenges of urban growth with decisive solutions. To speak of sanitary reform in such political terms may sound strange. Virchow himself admitted that there was no "liberal" way to clean gutters and empty waterclosets.[177] Moreover, until the arrival of the Social Democrats well into the last quarter of the nineteenth century, municipal government in Germany was ostensibly apolitical: it was part of the ideology of self-government that urban liberal politics claimed to represent the general interest.[178]

Such claims are the surest strength of an ideology, and conceal the particular concerns that in fact motivate it. In sewerage reform, urban liberals could claim to have improved the living conditions of every inhabitant of the city without having sacrificed any of their own power. Canalization effected concrete change, and radically transformed the image of the city abroad, without any redistribution of wealth among classes or any inordinate encroachment on property rights or individual liberties. It also proved that reason, in the form of scientific expertise as well as administrative consistency, provided the basis of a well-run government. Canalization, therefore, fit admirably within the goals and abilities of liberal reformers in Germany, and Virchow acknowledged his debt to the governmental context for reform that Berlin had offered him. On several occasions he had compromised with the condominium of urban liberalism – in his economic justifications for canalization, his collaboration with Hobrecht, and his acceptance of the Magistrat's somewhat undemocratic initiative. But in a parliamentary speech of 1883 Virchow justified this accommodation:

As a city councilman ... I have accomplished many useful and practical things, in which on a national level I would have found no support; in part because national politics was closed for me, I turned to the municipal community in order to do much good. I have found there a forum that pleases me: I have established hospitals, built schools, laid out sewers and irrigation fields. I have accomplished a lot of useful things, not out of ambition, but rather because they have given me deep satisfaction.[179]

To explain why Virchow did not find the same "support" in national politics will be the aim of the next chapter.

Chapter 4

Virchow in Parliament:
The Frustrations of National Health Politics

Liberal social science in a conservative state

The story of Virchow's parliamentary activity in health politics is plagued by an annoying gap. On 31 May 1883 the German Reichstag approved Europe's first national sickness insurance law, the earliest in a series of three "social insurance" measures inaugurated in the last years of Bismarck's chancellorship (the other two dealt with industrial accidents and old age/disability). By 1885 the sickness insurance funds already covered 10 per cent of the population, a proportion that had doubled by 1904.[180] In 1888, the funds paid out 61.5 million marks in medical expenses.[181] Sickness insurance was in fact the most substantial health programme undertaken by the German government in the nineteenth century. One would therefore expect Virchow to have been passionately involved in the debate on the bill, but in parliament he barely mentioned the subject. Though by 1883 he had held his Reichstag seat for three years, Virchow did not once rise to discuss the bill's provisions. During his entire tenure in the Reichstag (1880–93) and in the Prussian parliament (1862–1902), he only spoke on sickness insurance three times – eight years after the initial bill, at that.[182] We know that he was on hand to vote against the bill in May 1883, but the reasons for his silence up until then remain a mystery.[183] Still, it is worthwhile to attempt a reconstruction of his views on the subject, because the circumstances of Virchow's non-participation shed light on his broader problems in national health care reform. In particular, they reveal the reasons that account for his unsuccessful bid for liberal health politics in the parliamentary matters in which he did take an active part. This will be the main subject of this chapter.

The sickness insurance law offered much that Virchow could have supported.[184] It provided for a very decentralized network of local insurance funds largely independent of state influence. Both workers and their employers contributed to the funds, with the workers contributing twice as much as the employers and holding twice as many seats in the funds' steering committees. The leadership of the funds was authorized to contract with a body of physicians who would provide medical services for the workers. In at least a schematic sense, therefore, the sickness insurance funds resembled the medical charity associations Virchow had advocated in 1848–9: they ensured local self-government, they administered free care to disadvantaged labourers, and they provided a choice among doctors. On the other hand, the structure of the funds betrayed its origins in an illiberal political philosophy such as Bismarck's. The law compelled all workers in the trades it covered[185] to join the sickness funds, in direct contrast to the voluntary association that provided so much inspiration for Virchow's politics. In fact, the funds were not so much associational in structure as corporatist. Instead of bringing together representatives of a single interest – and then pitting this interest against others in a democratic interchange – the funds joined employers and workers together in a single organization. This arrangement forced cooperation and made workers' interest in health care contingent upon a satisfactory accommodation with their employers. Thus despite their numerical predominance in the funds' leadership, workers could easily lose the kind of antagonistic stance necessary in Virchow's conception of pluralistic politics.

Contemporary German experience proves that the corporatist principle of codetermination (*Mitbestimmung*) is not incompatible with a liberal system of government, so this feature of the sickness insurance funds did not necessarily represent the kiss of death to Virchow. He may have been able to stomach his objections to the funds, in the same way that he compromised on certain points in the canalization of Berlin. Thus, what made the 1883 sickness insurance law unpalatable for Virchow was most likely not its form *per se*. What made it unacceptable was that its structure aimed at stabilizing a conservative political system he deeply distrusted. By directing workers' aspirations into depoliticized corporatist funds, Bismarck hoped to prove the state's interest in their plight without endangering the state through their participation in politics. His government had set forth this philosophy as early as 1881: "a duty of *state-preserving policy* should be to cultivate the *conception* – and that, too, amongst the non-propertied classes, which form at once the most numerous and the least instructed part of the population – that the state is not merely a necessary but a beneficent institution".[186]

Contemporary historians have used such pronouncements to attack the widespread view of Bismarckian social insurance as "the first all-encompassing social policy package in modern society" and the germ of the welfare state.[187] Hans-Ulrich Wehler, for instance, has argued that Bismarck regarded social insurance as a component of his manipulative "carrot-and-stick" policy towards the working classes. To soften the impact of the repressive Anti-Socialist Law of 1878, Bismarck introduced social insurance as a "sugar coating" to the "bitter pill" of worker repression.[188]

Other scholars deny Bismarck's progressivism with less cynical interpretations, suggesting simply that he was not really interested in social insurance, deriding the true effectiveness of the programmes, and searching for precedents in German history that make Bismarck's conservative coup in social legislation seem less revolutionary.[189] Neither school of opinion, however, has adequately explored the crucial weakness in the claim that Bismarck's legislation was truly visionary: why did the liberals exert such a negligible influence on its passage? If the modern welfare state is based on liberal principles – albeit modified from their original, classical form – how can such a conservative figure as Bismarck be seen as one of its founders?

Historians have treated the liberals' stance on social insurance in an essentially dismissive fashion. This is certainly not surprising, because most German liberals had very little to contribute to social legislation anyway. The moderate National Liberals could claim to have supported the 1883 bill, but, as Dieter Langewiesche argues, only at the expense of an alliance with Bismarck "that verged on illiberalism". On the other hand, the left-wing Progressives – Virchow's party – opposed sickness insurance, allegedly from "Manchesterian liberal blindness" and a belief in "economic Darwinism". In sum, both camps failed to influence social policy because "there was no comprehensive political-social reform block in German liberalism".[190] Virchow's philosophy dictated, however, that political liberalism and a social safety-net were in fact complementary. His opposition to the conservative rationale inspiring sickness insurance was based on subtler objections than most other (leftist) liberals offered.[191]

Specifically, the organization of health care in Germany pitted Virchow's liberal social science against an ideology that I will call "conservative state interventionism". The primary aim of this type of statecraft is to enhance the prestige and power of the state, and only secondarily to address matters of the public interest, such as health care. Sickness insurance, with its statist rationale, is but the clearest instance of a more general "state-preserving policy". Since true social reform is not its goal, the state finds shortcuts to bolster its power that forego what Virchow considered a rational organization of social programmes. Intervention must be decisive yet limited; control, preservation, and economy are more important than thoroughness, efficiency, and consistency.[192] This ideology is the flipside of Virchow's liberal reformism, which subordinates state power to political principles and the public good. Interventionism in Virchow's mind was not defined by the need to preserve the state, but rather the need to preserve liberal values, the highest of which was that a liberal government can and must provide the material (and medical) basis for freedom, education and prosperity. It was the tension between these rival ideologies that thwarted the dedicated pursuit of liberal health care reform by Virchow. Virchow's silence on sickness insurance, with its explicitly statist rationale and distorted, corporatist organization, exemplifies this tension, but in the other matters that did claim his interest one sees the same dilemma.

This chapter will articulate Virchow's liberal critique of German health care with reference to the two tenets of his social science: first, that the state must accept responsibility for health by constructing a rational and organized public health administration; and second, that the state should leave the actual practice of healing as much as possible in the hands of the physician-élite, which alone was qualified to bear the burden of social leadership for health care. To Virchow, Bismarck's conservative political system distorted the proper relations among science, the medical profession, and the organs of government that were dictated by liberal social science. Virchow's parliamentary speeches support this argument by showing his reaction to specific health policies that arose in legislative debates. A methodological caveat is necessary before proceeding, however. The very circumstance that prevented his sustained and consistent parliamentary activity in health politics also makes it necessary to treat Virchow's sporadic utterances somewhat outside of their particular context. Only by focusing on the body of speeches as a whole is it possible to avoid a belaboured discussion of their specific settings, and to trace the broader theme of the distortion of German medical politics by conservative ideology.[193]

The growth of medical science: reformist possibilities, conservative limitations

This distortion is clearest in the progress of medical science in the last half of the nineteenth century. This period witnessed great leaps in the scientific understanding of disease, spawning movements aimed at applying new medical theories to public health reform. In a sense, Virchow came into his own. His progressive politics and all-encompassing idea of social medicine still put him far left of centre, but he was much less of a loner on the fringe. In 1867, the Assembly of German Natural Scientists and Physicians created a special section devoted to hygiene and public health. Two years later, the *German Quarterly for Public Health Care*[194] published its first issue and soon became the most influential journal for public health reform in Germany. Finally, in 1873, the advocates of progressive medicine founded a national organization, the German Association for Public Health, to carry their reformist message.

From the outset, these organizations justified public health intervention in more conservative terms than Virchow used. Instead of appealing to the ethical right to health enjoyed by each individual, for example, the leaders of the awakening public health movement pointed to the economic and social advantages of sanitary reform. Max von Pettenkofer, the Munich professor and guru of municipal sanitation, believed that "illness is an object that can be expressed in figures" and attempted to calculate the numerical value of health to a community.[195] Carl Reclam, one of the editors of the *German Quarterly*, articulated this principle more philosophically on the first page of the journal's premiere issue:

It is not the task of public health to look after the long life or well-being of each individual – rather, it should secure and promote the capacities of the entire population ... In that health care aims at providing all citizens without exception with the physical foundation of a prosperous development, it serves commercial life: because the productive power of the state rests on the capacity of individuals.[196]

In parliament, Virchow pragmatically accepted such arguments about health care. As long as the ends remained the same, he willingly endorsed both economic and ethical justifications. In two speeches from 1868, he advocated health reform from a "national-economic standpoint" while simultaneously defending the ethical "right to existence that every person has with respect to the state".[197]

More ominous for the conservative direction of public health was its depoliticization, which began soon after the first wave of activism of the late 1860s. Most of this first wave had centred on municipal sanitary reform, and with the success of projects like Berlin's canalization it became an accepted fact, instead of a political claim, that communities had an obligation to provide for public health. Advocates of a politicized medicine therefore partly lost the "beachhead" that urban reform could have offered for the conquest of national health politics.[198] Public health simply became more technical and professional. At the German Hygienic Exhibition in Berlin in 1883, scientists and administrators showcased everything from safely designed schooldesks and bathtubs to the latest methods of food inspection and groundwater investigation.[199] To be sure, some dedicated physicians and scientists besides Virchow continued to carry the banner of political medicine. Alfred Grotjahn, the author of *Social Pathology*, who was influenced by the reformist ideas of the liberal Gustav Schmoller, dedicated his life to a practical science of "social hygiene" but as a socialist never lost touch with politics.[200]

The model physician of Imperial Germany was not Alfred Grotjahn, nor certainly Virchow, but Robert Koch. If Virchow spent his formative years behind a barricade, Koch spent his behind a microscope. He was the incarnation of the diligent, thoroughly professional, apolitical scientist. Moreover, Koch's theory of bacteriology was not only one of the most important medical breakthroughs of the nineteenth century, but also pregnant with conservative political implications. Specifically, the now familiar idea that disease owes its origins to infectious micro-organisms focused medical interventions very narrowly on specific biological causes. In contrast to Virchow's all-encompassing etiology, which admitted social as well as biological factors, Koch's theory concerned local and individual pathogens exclusively. Curing patients did not involve radical changes in their social milieu; rather, strictly biomedical remedies would suffice.

Popular memory has fixated on the conflict between Koch's and Virchow's ideas, and on Virchow's reluctance to accept the bacteriological theory, but contemporary scholarship downplays their differences.[201] Virchow, in fact, had nothing against Koch's theory in itself. He merely thought it dangerous to accept it as the sole basis for either medical science or health politics. From a scientific standpoint, Virchow believed that many infectious diseases could not be traced to a "bacillus", and for policy reasons he faulted the belief that "with the discovery of a bacillus everything necessary has been done to do away with a disease". Virchow believed it was imperative that practical achievements complement theoretical discoveries. He argued against the needless proliferation of university chairs and institutes for bacteriology and hygiene, and instead stressed the success of practical innovations, such as the antiseptic revolution in surgery, that came primarily through direct experience. Above all, it was necessary to apply all available medical knowledge to public health programmes that tangibly affected the health of society.[202]

Practical public health: conservative state intervention and Virchow's liberal alternative

Koch's theory did in fact furnish the spirit and a good deal of the substance for tangible reform, but not in ways that Virchow fully accepted. Koch's ideas simply fit in better with the ideology of conservative state interventionism. First, the international fame that his bacteriological theory enjoyed underscored the easy prestige that pure scientific discovery could win for the German state. The Reich graciously funded Koch's and other scientists' theoretical researches, and showed its gratitude by inducting him into the Order of the Crown, Second Class.[203] In so doing, the government not only acknowledged a great German physician, but also symbolically identified Koch's advances with the progress of the German nation. Second and more concretely, the isolation of infectious micro-organisms opened up a whole realm for decisive yet conservative health programmes. The passage of commercial regulations on meat and milk inspection,[204] the extension of vaccination programmes to a large segment of the population,[205] and the erection of border and shipping controls and local disinfection centres to stop the spread of epidemics like cholera[206] attest not only to medicine's ability to apply the bacteriological theory to practical matters, but also to the state's willingness to extend its influence on society in a conservative fashion. None of these programmes substantially interfered with the economic or social life of the population, nor certainly did they embrace the kind of social reform Virchow advocated.

Virchow applauded these developments in so far as they finally signalled the progress of medicine in concrete public health programmes. He shared with the Reich authorities a nationalistic pride in Koch's achievements.[207] Virchow himself isolated the organism responsible for trichinosis (which affected pork), and supervised the construction of meat inspection facilities in Berlin that provided the model for national legislation.[208] Finally, he approved of state intervention on a philosophical level. He regarded compulsory vaccinations as an "eminently appropriate matter for the state" because of the consistency and thoroughness that a truly nationwide vaccination programme could offer. Measures designed to prevent epidemics similarly required a broad-based and coordinated effort to eradicate the spread of disease.[209]

If Virchow agreed with some of the individual public health programmes undertaken by the government, he also made it clear that the conservative state interventionism that inspired it was useful only to a certain point. The shirking of its responsibilities in chronically underdeveloped regions of the country proved to Virchow that the state did not truly conceive of the public good as the ultimate aim of health reform. Repeatedly referring in parliament to the example of Upper Silesia in 1848, Virchow demanded increased state financial and medical assistance to combat epidemics and hunger that periodically threatened both Silesia and other disadvantaged areas, like East Prussia. Instead of its traditional and irresponsible advocacy of private charity, the state should act to compensate for the deficiencies of local aid. Maintaining that its "appeal to self-help is the surest sign of ... the insufficiencies of a province" and the inadequacy of local initiative, he advocated a swift response to "extraordinary circumstances" that temporarily disabled such initiative. Importantly, the state's response should avoid "overwhelming" localities, and focus instead on sowing the seeds for a more capable local self-help should future depredations occur. This the government would accomplish through its unique power to equalize gross inconsistencies among different provinces, by redistributing tax revenues, and through its gentle nurturing of local self-government in backward areas where the "historical feeling" for such an institution was weakly developed. In sum, the proper sphere of government lay in fostering the liberal local institutions that would ensure a truly effective "self-help".[210]

Virchow was referring here to the intermittent opportunities that governments had to eradicate chronic and repetitive misfortunes, but he also applied his belief in responsible liberal government to the day-to-day institutions of public health, whose organization he found slipshod and ineffectual. He focused particular blame on the activities of the Imperial Health Office, created in 1876 to coordinate all health affairs for the Empire. As defined by its charter, the mandate of the Office included advising the Chancellor on pertinent health matters, drafting medical legislation, monitoring public health developments in foreign countries, and collecting medical statistics on the Reich.[211] In 1881 Virchow declared that the Office was not living up to its mandate. Since its founding, he argued, the Office's staff had been enticed into investigations on the cutting edge of medicine instead of the humdrum task of preparing practical legislative suggestions. The published reports from the Office contained unsigned and controversial scientific articles that more properly belonged in medical journals. The seduction by theory betokened a deeper neglect of those practical activities that alone contributed to an effective public health administration.[212]

From the top down, the organs of health administration evidenced a similar irresponsibility. To Virchow, a liberal state recognized that a responsible administration conducted its affairs rationally and efficiently, and he maintained as late as 1895 that "we cannot say that the Reich has an orderly set of laws to refer to in its interventions. The German Reich possesses to this day no law that exactly spells out the boundaries of power and responsibility for the individual administrative authorities".[213] He claimed that a proper delineation of state authority must join medical knowledge with executive power. Doctors should replace jurists at the head of public health organizations; they should be exempted from the "foreign influences" of the police; and the whole organization of public health should be moved from the competence of the Cultural Ministry and placed under the aegis of the Interior Ministry. This change would not only eliminate the "confessional" prejudices under which medicine suffered in the Cultural Ministry, but also provide "everything necessary for the present organization of medical affairs", namely a powerful administration.[214] The handling of veterinary medicine, whose organization had enjoyed such improvements, demonstrated what the marriage of science and executive authority could accomplish in such areas as meat inspection and the prevention of animal epidemics.[215]

Virchow reserved special attention for the intermediate and lower levels of public health organization. In 1868 he presented a specific proposal for reform, in which he emphasized that the traditional tasks for regional public health authorities in Prussia needed a redefinition for modern times.[216] The customary duties of state physicians in Prussia – performing autopsies and rendering expert medical opinions in court cases – struck him as increasingly anachronistic. The state could better allocate its resources by transferring emphasis from forensic medicine to the "medical police" (*medizinische Polizei*), a term that in German refers not to law enforcement but to the state's entire low-level regulatory apparatus. The medical police regulated the sale of food and drugs, oversaw vaccination programmes, collected medical statistics, inspected homes and businesses, monitored the spread of infectious diseases and supervised disinfection and sanitation measures, and generally transmitted legal and administrative orders on health care into practical effect.[217] To implement this reorientation towards a greater executive competence, Virchow advocated a two-tiered organizational reform. On the regional level, the governmental medical councils (along with local "sanitary commissions"), which had medical police functions, should replace the obsolescent provincial medical colleges, whose purely advisory role in public health affairs and preoccupation with medical jurisprudence made them unnecessary.[218] On the local level, Virchow favoured the consolidation of the offices of county physician (*Kreisphysikus*) and county surgeon (*Kreiswundarzt*)[219] into one position with police authority, not simply because only one official was necessary to do the job, but also because he could then be paid twice as much. On this lowest and most despised public health official[220] depended the effectiveness of all practical regulations emanating from the higher Prussian and German authorities. Into the 1870s Virchow used his influence on the Budget Commission in the Prussian legislature to press continually for higher salaries for the county doctors, because he was "convinced that the government is obligated to appoint officials who at least have a safe enough existence that they do not have to turn to private practice" and who will therefore be free to "promote an effective public health [administration] necessary in the interest of the people".[221]

The government did not implement Virchow's public health reform. The best it could do was to offer in 1872 a modest pay rise for the county doctors, the foot-soldiers of public health, and cover their train trips and other expenses incurred in the discharge of their duties.[222] In the opinion of most contemporaries, the top-heavy, overly theoretical, and poorly organized administration of public health in Germany remained an obstacle to meaningful reform throughout the nineteenth century.[223] Conservative state interventionism simply did not have the commitment to the nuts and bolts of organizational reform that Virchow advocated.

The medical profession and its dependence on the state

Virchow's concern for empowering the country doctors had aimed at enhancing the state's ability to undertake meaningful public health reform on the grassroots level. The sheer scope of government health programmes, however, required it to step outside its network of official state physicians.

In its vaccination programmes, the government relied upon quasi-official doctors certified to administer inoculations;[224] and in the sickness insurance funds, local fund directors contracted with semi-private physicians who provided medical care for insured workers.[225] Most significantly, the ongoing medicalization of the population increased the importance of decisions on whether and how to test, license and police a body of private physicians growing in size and influence. From 1827 to 1887 the proportion of state-employed physicians dropped from 49 per cent (out of 1,919) to only 12 per cent (out of 15,824).[226] The development of a relationship between the (private) medical profession and the government did not occur in a context of free negotiation between equals. Unlike the American example, where the profession grew almost autonomously of state influence,[227] professional consolidation in Germany took place under the tutelage and direction of the state. This entangled, obtrusive, and sometimes stormy relationship was for Virchow the most grievous instance of a misdirected conservative state interventionism. In parliament he focused particular activity on freeing the profession from what he believed was an oppressive and illiberal system.

The state's paternalistic relationship to the medical profession had continued unabated after the medical reform movement in 1848–9. In 1852 it finally granted traditional doctors the right to practise in all spheres of medicine, from surgery to internal medicine to obstetrics.[228] This act set a precedent by tying professional improvement to state initiative and succeeded in winning the support of many doctors. Virchow was prominent among the minority that continued to oppose state tutelage. In 1860, he helped lead the Berlin Medical Society, whose constituency had been liberal at least since 1848–9, to demand an end to the onerous state interference represented by its anti-quackery laws and provisions for forced medical treatment by doctors.[229] The political influence of the Berlin society enabled one of its representatives to campaign successfully for an official acceptance of this demand soon after the founding of the North German Union (the precursor state to the Empire). In 1869 Reichstag representative Loewe (Virchow did not have a Reichstag seat at this time) reiterated the medical reformers' arguments about anti-quackery laws, holding them as ineffective and poorly enforced, and asked for their abolition as a *de jure* acknowledgement of *de facto* conditions of free competition that had long obtained in Germany.[230] Later that year, the German Trade Ordinance made medicine an unregulated trade and preserved only the title of "doctor" (*Arzt*) as the legally protected privilege of state-licensed physicians.[231]

The objection of the profession as a whole did not become manifest until several years after the Trade Ordinance, because physicians were still not well-organized. The very organizational immaturity that made traditional doctors fear free competition from natural healers, homeopaths, and plain quacks also made an articulate rebuttal against Virchow's camp in the Berlin Society all but impossible. Finally, however, the German Union of Medical Societies was formed in 1873 for the stated purpose of defending the profession's interests through a demand that the state organize and officially sanction representative organs for the entire medical profession. Seven years later the Union explicitly demanded the re-regulation of medical practice through the abrogation of the relevant sections in the Trade Ordinance.[232] In 1882, at its annual meeting, the union representatives drafted a list of "Fundamentals for a German Medical Ordinance" that further clarified the dominant strain of professional opinion: doctors should retain trade freedoms that concerned the actual exercise of their practices (including the collection of fees), but should become subject to state-sanctioned medical boards that would replace unrestricted practice with a collegial supervision that embraced disciplinary measures against derelict physicians.[233]

These developments put Virchow in the odd position of defending his profession against what he viewed as its own Faustian short-sightedness. Throughout the 1880s he campaigned in parliament against the profession's demands for a return to protective regulatory legislation. In this crusade, Virchow returned to his claim from 1848–9 that the medical profession, like all other groups in society, functioned best when its energies were granted free reign. This advocacy of an empowered élite sprang from a personal belief in the nobility and benevolent social influence of the medical profession. As he admitted in 1883, "I am somewhat seduced by the experiences I have had in my own occupation". His admiration for the heroic enterprise of medicine led him to assert its right to a privileged political standing, since the reciprocal "claims" that were in turn made upon physicians "in many cases exceed what is demanded of other persons, in civilian life".[234] Carrying such a high moral burden, doctors should be as exempt as possible from state regulation, because in general, "doctors have on the whole devoted themselves to an honourable life" and therefore needed no regulation. To be sure, the state had a role in abetting doctors in their medical pursuits, but this influence should be confined to "cooperation", not regulation. With regard to the state's interest in assuring a well-organized profession, Virchow held that doctors' "intelligence" plus their "human feeling" would bring them to organize themselves.[235] This unswerving – and, it must be said, uncritical – dedication to a free medical profession is a clear example of his personal tendency towards espousing simple political dogmas. None the less, the frustrations that this libertarian position entailed stemmed not so much from his personal quirks as from his commitment to liberal social science. The chances for professional freedom as the precondition for the physician-élite's exalted and benevolent social role were undermined by the complex history of professional politics, which tended ever more towards government meddling.

In 1886–7 Virchow experienced his first major disappointment in the struggle against state regulation of the medical profession. Even as he continued to speak out in parliament against the "guildlike" organization of the profession, expressing his fear of "bureaucratic power",[236] the Prussian government was preparing a reversal of the passive stance it had taken ever since professional deregulation in 1869. In 1887, following the demands of the doctors' union and the lead of other German *Länder* – Baden in 1864, followed by Saxony, Brunswick, Bavaria, Württemberg, and Hessen – Prussia bypassed parliament and issued a decree establishing medical boards to represent all physicians within its borders.[237] The structure and authority of the boards did not in themselves betray overweening state influence. Doctors presided over the boards (and of course formed their constituency), and though a state official would be present at their meetings, he would exercise no vote in the proceedings, the main reason for his presence being to prevent abuse of disciplinary privileges by doctors against their colleagues.[238] The main purpose of the organizations was simply to bring doctors together to discuss professional matters, attain a unified voice in subjects of professional interest, furnish expert opinions on public health matters to the relevant state officials, and provide financial support from a common fund to physicians who were struggling in their practices (through the so-called *Umlagerecht*). But even these activities conferred substantial state-supported political power on the profession, and therefore the mere fact of the state's initiative in setting up the boards represented for Virchow an unacceptable meddling.[239]

What made the boards truly intolerable, however, was the extension of disciplinary jurisdiction against malpracticing doctors in the 1890s. In the original decree of 1887, disciplinary procedure was limited to denying errant physicians the right to vote in board decisions.[240] But in 1892, with the support of the doctors' union,[241] a commission of representatives from the Prussian medical boards declared its support for disciplinary councils (*Ehrengerichte*) whose powers would still be limited to disfranchisement and fines, but which for the first time would enjoy a quasi-legal standing and possibly include lawyers, as well as doctors, as judges on the tribunals. The commission's vote was ten in favour, two against, Virchow being one of the dissenters.[242] In parliament that year, Virchow vented his aggravation with supporters of the tribunals like Dr Eduard Graf who believed that a "more guildlike" organization of the profession would, through enforcement of discipline, increase the "esteem of the German public" for the medical community.[243] Through the rest of the decade discussions continued, during which time Virchow led the Berlin Medical Society in opposition to the tribunals, in contrast to twelve Prussian medical boards who supported them.[244] Finally, in 1899, the government promulgated a law establishing the tribunals with the support of most of the legislature.[245] Virchow again spoke for the minority when he maintained that the small number of disciplinary cases did not warrant state intervention to preserve doctors' honour and stated that the government's vague definition of what constituted malpractice would lead to "arbitrariness" in judgements. Finally, he reiterated his belief in the necessity of a free and liberal association of doctors, in which publicity, openness and debate would provide all the necessary force required to bring delinquent physicians in to line.[246]

Virchow failed to realize that the disciplinary councils merely laid the keystone in the conservative professional-governmental complex that developed under the aegis of an interventionist, regulating state in the nineteenth century. Disciplinary jurisdiction was the link that joined the political organization of the medical profession to the policing power in which both doctors and the state had an interest. Physicians wished to exclude competition from quacks, and the state claimed the right of intervention in the name of securing quality in medical care. At the same time, this cosy condominium of shared interest exhibited serious fault lines, as is illustrated by the growth of sickness insurance funds after 1883. The establishment of sickness insurance constituted the single most important development in the history of professional politics in the last quarter of the nineteenth century. The scheme's provision, allowing local funds to contract with physicians to dispense medical treatment, demonstrated just how entangled and conflicting the two interests had become in the Empire. The state-sanctioned insurance funds, in their desire to minimize costs by increasing control over physicians – who enjoyed a monopoly on deciding which patients counted as "sick" and what treatment they needed – attempted to restrict the number of doctors who were allowed to treat fund members. In turn, physicians, who competed heavily for slots as fund doctors, protested against these restrictions and demanded "free doctor choice" for patients.[247] By 1900, a vociferous new pressure group, the so-called Leipziger Verband, had been formed, and it resorted to physician strikes to defend professional interests.[248]

It is in this context that Virchow's minimal contribution to the debate on sickness insurance finally becomes important. In two speeches of 1891–2 he attempted to bolster the profession's position and restrict competition for fund slots.[249] Specifically, he advocated an end to the practice of recognizing natural healers (*Naturärzte*) who were not licensed medical doctors but who had acquired a *de facto* right to dispense care in many insurance funds.[250] He went so far as to propose an amendment to the 1883 law (which was being revised at that time anyway) legally restricting uncertified healers from participating in the funds.[251] This stance appears to be a lapse of his traditional objection to state patronage, but actually makes sense given the logic of the 1869 deregulation he had helped propose, which had allowed free medical practice but protected the title of doctor. In his opposition to natural healers he was merely following his conventional argument that the state must tolerate such freedom but not actively sanction it. He said it would be a "disloyal procedure" if the state failed to support traditional doctors in this instance, and stated that he "would regard it as a great loss if through a hesitant activity the doctors' position, which it has recently won, would become lost".[252]

Though true to his own philosophy, Virchow underestimated the scale of the larger professional politics in which he played a part. In petitioning for the exclusion of natural healers (in which enterprise he failed, incidentally[253]), he unwittingly advanced claims appropriate not only for his particular conception of "liberal" state-profession relations, but also for the greater political struggle connected with the problems of an interlocking and unstable association between the government and the medical community. In political reality, if not in his own mind, he therefore relied on the conservative state interventionism that had guided the development of this association since before 1848. This fact can only serve to underline the lack of a suitable context characterizing Virchow's national health politics. His cogent critique of state irresponsibility and disorganization in its own public health affairs does contrast with his ultimate failure to grasp the political significance of professional regulation in insurance funds, after so many years of resistance to such regulation. Whether he was pointing out the flaws in an illiberal state or exhibiting his idolization of a healing profession, Virchow demonstrated the inapplicability of his liberal health politics in a climate of conservative state interventionism. The twin tasks of national health politics – public health and professional regulation – offered opportunities for Virchow's liberal social science, with its emphasis on state sponsorship of health programmes and collaboration with a freely constituted élite, but the failures of liberalism to stamp its political forms on the German State rendered such opportunities ultimately fruitless.

Chapter 5

Virchow and the Legacy
of German Liberalism

The past two centuries have witnessed a profound shift in the meaning of liberalism: from a nineteenth-century ideology based on individual freedoms, *laissez-faire* economics, and limited government to a twenty-first-century worldview embracing welfare programmes, economic management and state intervention. What light can Rudolf Virchow's career shed on this development? As early as 1848, Virchow had developed a political philosophy marrying classical liberal principles with a governmental responsibility for social well-being. He then applied this ideological synthesis to health reform activities throughout his life. One could therefore regard Virchow, with his innovative brand of medical politics, as a transitional figure in the broad history of Western liberalism. It is rare, however, for any German liberal to be seen in this way, as a forerunner to the modern progressive. For in German history it is impossible to speak of the prolonged transition from "classical" to "welfare state" liberalism without reference to the tremendous upheaval that punctuates it: National Socialism. Far from seeing in nineteenth-century German liberalism the seeds of the modern welfare state, scholars have identified its failure as a political movement as one of the primary preconditions for Nazism's rise. Before situating my specific arguments on Virchow's socially progressive philosophy into German liberalism at large, it is therefore necessary to address liberalism's troubled past.

Ralf Dahrendorf's 1967 question crystallizes the problem of liberal failure: "Why is it that so few in Germany embraced the principle of liberal democracy?" To him, nineteenth-century liberals failed to erect a political system based on equality, pluralism, institutionalized conflict and "public virtues". This deficiency meant that Germany's pre-industrial, authoritarian political structures survived largely unmodified into the twentieth century and ultimately helped Hitler to power.[254] Many scholars of Dahrendorf's generation have supported his basic view of liberal complicity in a "faulted nation". The collapse of liberal-democratic ambitions in the 1848 revolution, followed by the liberal defeat in the so-called Constitutional Conflict of

1862–6, are said to have revealed two crucial weaknesses in liberal politics. First, the liberals failed to curry enough support with the masses to mount an effective campaign against the forces of reaction. According to Theodore Hamerow's analysis of the 1848 revolution, their espousal of *laissez-faire* economic and social doctrines alienated artisans who stood to lose a great deal through the abolition of guild privileges, and their unwillingness to sacrifice the liberal right to property drove away peasants who believed that revolutionary expropriation and agrarian reform were the only solutions for their hunger.[255] James Sheehan and others have argued that the liberal party lacked a sufficient social base to stage a muscular opposition against Bismarck's unconstitutional appropriation of state funds for the military in 1862–6. Despite the backing of an impressive number of ancillary bourgeois political organizations, the liberals still feared losing the support of the *Volk* at large, and this led them to cave in to Bismarck when he offered national unification as a quid pro quo for their acquiescence in his illegal rule.[256] With the increasing importance of mass politics after the 1860s and 1870s, the party of *Bildung und Besitz* (education and property) never fully overcame its roots in an elitist political outlook. In fact, during this period, the history of the liberal parties revolved more around their internal fragmentation than their weakened claim to represent society as a whole.

The second failure of German liberalism is much more damning, because it points to its ideological predisposition to romanticize an authoritarian state. According to scholars like Otto Pflanze and Leonard Krieger, what made it so easy for liberals to succumb to Bismarck in 1866 was their deep-seated admiration of his power.[257] Pflanze suggests that the seminal choice of a powerful, unified Bismarckian state over a liberal legal state (or *Rechtsstaat*) was conditioned by liberals' statist inclinations and social weakness. Their "capitulation" in 1866

had been prepared for more than a century in the development of the German liberal tradition. Its origin lay in the delayed growth of the German middle class, the peculiar coupling of freedom and authority ... the Hegelian deification of the state, and the romantic glorification of force. The liberals were the victims of their own limited ends, their lack of genuine support, and their lust for national power ... Never had they aimed at full responsibility for the management of public affairs.[258]

Devoid of popular resonance – so the argument goes – the liberals fled into the arms of a powerful nation-state whose semi-constitutional structure provided no guarantee against an authoritarian political system careering towards the Nazi catastrophe of the next century. In a very provocative formulation, Hans-Ulrich Wehler has characterized the "sham constitutionalism" resulting from the liberal capitulation as the ideological complement to the deeper "structural" deficiencies that predisposed Germany to crisis, instability, and ultimately, dictatorship.[259]

This image of a lockstep march towards National Socialism has been sharply criticized in the last two decades. David Blackbourn and Geoff Eley have tried to reclaim the contingent nature of Imperial German politics from what they perceive as an overdetermined course of failure. In particular, they take issue with the common view that the spinelessness of the German bourgeoisie is to blame for liberalism's defeat in high politics. Eley disputes the "conceptual slippage" between the middle class and its putative ideology, an elision that "ascribes to the bourgeoisie as a class the set of values (liberalism) that according to the textbook it should have held".[260] Both Eley and Blackbourn proceed to flesh out a sphere of peculiarly bourgeois politics. Eley, for example, defends German industrialists' illiberal "right-wing" politics as the product of "capitalist rationality" instead of bourgeois failure. Blackbourn concentrates more on a "silent bourgeois revolution" and a subtly hidden "shadow society" upon which the bourgeoisie imprinted its class interest without the constitutional changes in high politics associated with liberal ideology. To some extent, this decoupling of bourgeois politics from the fortunes of liberalism has cleared a space for the positive re-evaluation of liberalism's own strengths, especially in the "shadow" realm of culture and society.[261] More pronounced, however, is the tendency among scholars working in the wake of Blackbourn and Eley to rehabilitate *non-liberal* forms of bourgeois hegemony in German society. In so far as these scholars' interventions have rescued the bourgeoisie from a failed liberalism, they have to some extent left liberalism itself in the lurch.[262]

My approach is to claim for German liberalism a more nuanced history that is the political analogue to Blackbourn and Eley's model of a more socially complex and contingent German development in the nineteenth century.[263] Just as Blackbourn and Eley argue for a certain "rationality" in bourgeois politics – as a more sophisticated alternative to the argument that regards their illiberalism as a political miscalculation or moral lapse – so I am trying to explain German liberalism in terms of its own rational dynamic. I want to stress that the liberals' embrace of élitism and statism did not stem so much from their political timidity, ideological legacy, or inherent unpopularity as from the structural difficulties involved in applying liberal principles to German politics. It is in the realm of practical, as opposed to constitutional, politics that these structural conditions become clearest. The model of the "liberal social scientist", and specifically the career of Virchow, lend some rhyme and reason to the traditional liberal problems of social exclusivity and reliance upon the state, which have otherwise been interpreted in narrow moralizing terms.

In this study I have argued that Virchow's élitism was grounded in the belief that practical social reform could only be achieved by a body of selected leaders. In his early years Virchow acquired this perspective from the humanistic but paternalistic practice of medical healing, and this outlook carried him through the rest of his life. When he applied his liberal values to social politics, therefore, he was concerned to "heal" society – curing it through a radical dose of freedom, education and prosperity, but at the same time protecting it from an injurious social revolution. To effect this forceful but limited change it was necessary to place the dynamic energies of scientific rationality in the safe hands of an enlightened and activist élite. Viewed in this way, Virchow's élitism reflects not so much an estrangement from society as the conviction that it must enjoy some form of tutelary guidance. We saw this in his advocacy of an educated and indigenous leadership in Silesia for "medicine on a grand scale" there; in his struggle to make doctors the "natural advocates of the poor" through medical and professional reform; in his personal activity as the physician-reformer in Berlin's canalization; in his cooperation with a broader municipal leadership in the same project – with engineers like Hobrecht and Wiebe and with reformist laymen on the city council and Magistrat; and in his parliamentary campaigns for professional freedom. In all of these instances, Virchow believed that to bear the standard of social progress, the élite must exercise a more broadly diffused power than that wielded by an oppressively centralized state. His belief in a self-regulated medical profession based on the liberal model of the free association is the clearest application of this principle. But in general it was the liberal belief that society could manage its own affairs that led Virchow to promote an empowered élite free of state meddling.

At the same time as he campaigned for limiting government power, however, Virchow was inexorably led to invoke the state as a mediator between the reformist élite and the society it sought to elevate. Virchow's radical liberalism, and in particular his staunch opposition to Bismarck, prove that he was not succumbing here to some authoritarian impulse. Rather, he saw the construction of a rational, responsible government as the primary task of modern liberalism. Having witnessed the suffering in Silesia, Virchow had realized that a classical liberal ideology based on individual freedom is irrelevant in a society where individuals do not enjoy the material basis to exercise it. The progressive state that he envisioned protected liberal values precisely through its intervention in society, by gently uplifting the people. This meant that the state must balance its responsibility to promote a prosperous, liberal society with a strictly liberal conduct in its own affairs. In 1848–9 Virchow proclaimed this necessity in philosophical terms, and could only hint at its practical application, because the victory of the forces of reaction during the revolution dashed the chances for liberal governmental reform. But in Berlin he found a "state" – in the form of city government – congenial to his reformist impulses. Canalization was the ideal example of a health-conscious reform that imposed as little as possible on the free development of society. In parliament, Virchow further articulated his ideal of the progressive state: his idea of a state-sponsored public health emphasized the application of the rapidly growing science of medicine to health care reform. Specifically, he stressed the necessity of a "liberal" orchestration of state power and medical knowledge, coupled with a responsibility for disadvantaged areas and a rational and effective administration. Above all, the way to fashion a liberal state – and avoid dangerous meddling – lay in encouraging as far as possible the energies of an independent medical profession. But when Virchow's idea of a liberal government met up against a dominant ideology of conservative state interventionism, his national health politics languished in obscurity.

This view of liberal social science – and the logic of containment that binds liberal principles, an empowered élite, and a constitutional state – will, I hope, illustrate the dilemmas of German liberalism in a more sympathetic fashion than most scholarship allows. For one thing, it facilitates a renewed appreciation for German liberals' long-term contributions to the *Sozialstaat*, the post-World War II "social state" combining liberal constitutionalism with a social safety net. German social liberalism has long been the object of scholarly attention, whether as a missed opportunity to avoid the social fragmentation and political polarization of the Weimar Republic, or, more ominously, as a movement that itself succumbed to the nationalist and imperialist ideologies paving the way for Nazism.[264] In either case, this literature remains captive to peculiarly *German* concerns. Little attention has therefore been paid to Germany's impact on Western social liberalism as a whole. Historians working elsewhere, by contrast, have begun to realize just how many of the social-reformist departures in nineteenth-century Germany became incorporated into both the European and American progressive movements.[265] Virchow's career illustrates what was specifically *liberal* about these departures and the twentieth-century progressivism they helped to inspire. His activity combined the need to intervene in social affairs with the desire to preserve and promote individual rights, constitutional government, and the supremacy of reason. In so far as modern progressive movements also work within this framework, they owe their political origins to liberalism. Liberalism's contribution remains all the more powerful for being largely inconspicuous: that the modern welfare state incorporates these principles almost as articles of faith is a testament to its pervasive success.

Virchow's accomplishments shed fresh light on both the possibilities and the problems of social liberalism. In retrospect it is easy to perceive in Virchow the arrogance of the technocratic reformer or the naïveté of the egalitarian idealist, to name two vices plaguing many contemporary welfare-state liberals. Yet these judgements distort the nature of his achievement through the lens of twenty-first-century hindsight. They fail, in particular, to appreciate the ways scientism and humanism checked and tempered each other in Virchow's practical work. Science and the humanities, what C P Snow called the "two cultures" of twentieth-century intellectual life, enjoyed a much less antagonistic, mutually uncomprehending relation in Virchow's day. His liberal social science showed this. At the same time, his career offers us little guidance in understanding liberalism's relation to disciplines beyond his ken. Virchow showed little interest in the softer social sciences, like cultural anthropology, sociology and economics, where humanistic enquiry and technical analysis converge and compete most strongly. And while this deficit can hardly be faulted in a man whose dedication to other fields limited him to four hours' sleep a night, Virchow cleaved temperamentally to the certainties of hard-nosed empiricism, measuring skulls with calipers and scrutinizing cells under microscopes. He systematically avoided the fuzzy science of social criticism, where judgement, discretion and intuition were most needed. Unwittingly he conceded an entire spectrum of intellectual problems to the eugenicist and racist social thinkers who soon took them up. None the less, Virchow placed German medicine on an unshakeably scientific basis. His social science never lost touch with the material problems of human life. That his medical politics also inspired practical reforms of undeniable value secures his place in the development of a more humane Western liberalism.

Abbreviations

BKW	*Berliner klinische Wochenschrift*
CEPHE	*Collected Essays on Public Health and Epidemiology*
DVföG	*Deutsche Vierteljahrsschrift für öffentliche Gesundheitspflege*
MR	*Die medicinische Reform*
SBHA	*Stenographische Berichte über die Verhandlungen des Landtages, Haus der Abgeordneten*
SBR	*Stenographische Berichte über die Verhandlungen des Reichstags*
Virchow papers	Nachlaß Virchow, Zentrales Archiv, Akademie der Wissenschaften, Berlin

Note: Prussian Landtag and German Reichstag speeches (found in *SBHA* and *SBR* respectively) are cited by the date of the speech, the page numbers in the published proceedings, and the name of the speaker, as in the following example:

SBHA 9 Jan 1872, 299 (Virchow).

Notes

1 Rudolf Virchow, 'Der Armenarzt', *MR* 18 (3/11/1848): 125. For publication data, see bibliography.

2 Andrew Zimmerman offers a revisionist reading of this study in his recent article, 'Anti-Semitism as Skill: Rudolf Virchow's *Schulstatistik* and the Racial Composition of Germany', *Central European History* 32 (1999): 409–29.

3 Leon Eisenberg, 'Rudolf Ludwig Karl Virchow, Where Are You Now That We Need You?', *American Journal of Medicine* 77 (September 1984): 524–32.

4 Daniel Pridian, 'Rudolf Virchow and Social Medicine in Historical Perspective', *Medical History* 8 (1964): 274–8.

5 For a recap of Figlio's arguments, see George Silver, 'Virchow, The Heroic Model in Medicine: Health Policy by Accolade', *American Journal of Public Health* 77 (1987): 85–6; also Paul Weindling, 'Was Social Medicine Revolutionary? Rudolf Virchow and the Revolution of 1848', *Bulletin of the Society for the Social History of Medicine* 34 (1984): 13–18.

6 Erwin Ackerknecht, *Rudolf Virchow: Doctor, Statesman, Anthropologist* (New York: Arno Press, 1981), originally published by the University of Wisconsin Press in 1953.

7 The differences were spelt out by the German sociologist Max Weber at the beginning of the twentieth century, in his two canonical essays 'Politics as a Vocation' and 'Science as a Vocation', translated and reprinted in *From Max Weber: Essays in Sociology*, H H Gerth and C Wright Mills (eds) (New York: Oxford University Press, 1946), 77–128, 129–56 (respectively).

8 *SBHA* 18 Dec 1863, 507 (Bismarck).

9 Walter Bußmann, 'Rudolf Virchow und der Staat', in Helmut Berding (ed.), *Vom Staat des Ancien Régime zum modernen Parteistaat* (München: Oldenbourg, 1978), 279; Renato Mazzolini, *Politisch-biologische Analogien im Frühwerk Rudolf Virchows*, trans. Klaus-Peter Tieck (Marburg: Basilisken-Presse, 1988).

10 Richard Evans, *Death in Hamburg* (London: Penguin Books, 1990), 272–5; Byron Boyd, 'Rudolf Virchow. The Scientist as Politician' (PhD Diss., University of North Carolina, 1981), 144–6. Also in this vein, Paul Weindling, *Health, Race, and German Politics between National Unification and Nazism, 1870–1945* (Cambridge: Cambridge University Press, 1989), *passim*.

11 See Weindling, *Health, Race, and German Politics*, 36–59 on the Haeckel-Virchow dispute. Virchow also warned pointedly against putting Darwinian ideas into the heads of socialists.

12 To be sure, his famous essay on 'The Freedom of Science in the Modern State' can be read as asserting just such a division between empirical science and

political interests. Virchow aimed not only to protect science from political interference, but also to shield politics from the over-hasty appropriation of unproven scientific hypotheses (pre-eminently evolutionism). This logic, however, by no means precluded what Virchow saw as empirically-vetted scientfic truth from informing, even dictating, political decisions. His practical activities, as I argue in this book, illustrate this quite clearly. See Virchow's *Die Freiheit der Wissenschaft im modernen Staat* (Berlin: Wiegandt, Hempel & Parey, 1877).

13 Thus, if Ernst Haeckel represented the hierarchical, social Darwinist strain of mainstream bourgeois thought, Alfred Grotjahn, a leading proponent of the progressive "social hygiene" movement, came to embody the socialist alternative. On these and other figures, especially in the eugenics and racial hygiene movements whose rise paralleled radical nationalism, see Weindling, *Health, Race, and German Politics.*

14 Evans, *Death in Hamburg*, 274.

15 James Sheehan, *German Liberalism in the Nineteenth Century* (Chicago: University of Chicago Press, 1978); Dieter Langewiesche, *Liberalismus in Deutschland* (Frankfurt: Suhrkamp, 1988).

16 Rudolf Virchow, *Letters to His Parents, 1839 to 1864*, trans. L J Rather (Canton, Mass.: Watson Publishing International, 1990), 4–5.

17 Ibid., 17 (5/12/1839), 40 (14/5/1843), 59 (24/7/1845), 66–7 (25–28/5/1848).

18 Ibid., 69 (13/8/1846), 71–2 (1/5/1847), 75 (13/2/1848).

19 Ibid., 40 (14/5/1843).

20 Ibid., 41 (3/6/1843), 46 (30/7/1843).

21 Ibid., 40 (14/5/1843), 41 (3/6/1843).

22 Ibid., 46 (30/7/1843).

23 Ibid., 77 (24/2/1848).

24 Virchow, 'Report on the Typhus Epidemic in Upper Silesia' (1848), *CEPHE*, trans. L J Rather (Canton, Mass.: Watson Publishing International, 1985), vol. 1, 210.

25 Ibid., 210, 309–10.

26 Ibid., 217–18.

27 Ibid., 217–99.

28 Ibid., 297–8.

29 Ibid., 211.

30 Ibid., 211–13, 301–3, 308–9.

31 Ibid., 213, 215–16, 308–9.

32 Ibid., 307.

33 Ibid., 216–17, 307–8, 312–13, 317.

34 Ibid., 313, 315.

35 Ibid., 313.

36 Ibid., 216–17.

37 Virchow, *Letters*, 78–9 (29/2/1848).

38 Virchow, 'Report on the Typhus Epidemic', 307–8, 312, 314–17.

39 Ibid., 314, 316.

40 Ibid., 315–16, 318.

41 Ibid., 225, 282–3.

42 Ibid., 311–12.

43 Ibid., 217, 311.

44 Evidence for this paragraph comes from: Virchow, *Letters*, 80–86 (11–24/3/ 1848); *idem*, 'Was die "medicinische Reform" will', *MR* 1 (10/7/1848): 1–2. For publication data on *MR* (reprint) see the bibliography.

45 Erwin Ackerknecht, 'Beiträge zur Geschichte der Medizinalreform von 1848', *Sudhoffs Archiv für Geschichte der Medizin* 25 (1932): 80–81; Kurt Finkenrath, *Die Medizinalreform* (Leipzig: Johann Ambrosius Barth, 1929), 55–6; *MR* 14 (6/10/1848): 100.

46 *MR* 1 (10/7/1848): 3 for quotation and *passim* for reports on the General-Versammlung Berliner Aerzte.

47 On the Gesellschaft für wissenschaftliche Medicin and on the absence of professionally self-conscious medical associations before the revolution, see C Posner, 'Zur Geschichte des ärztlichen Vereinswesens in Berlin', *BKW* 30 (1893): 1230 and Eduard Graf, *Das ärztliche Vereinswesen in Deutschland und der deutsche Ärztevereinsbund* (Leipzig: F C W Vogel, 1890), 1–6, 138–41. The Gesellschaft für wissenschaftliche Medicin did exhibit some tendencies towards politicization during the revolution, though its debates remained extremely technical; still, its frequent discussions on a cholera epidemic of that year could not help but carry political overtones. See *MR, passim*.

48 See, for example, *MR*, 8, 42–4, 59–60, 65–8, 98–100, 114, 122–4, 151–2, 158–60, 167–8, 190–92, 195–6, 198–200, 203–4, 230–32, 250–52; also see Graf, *Das ärztliche Vereinswesen*, 16–17.

49 Steudel (1849), quoted in Ackerknecht, 'Beiträge', 95.

50 Oswa (1848), quoted in Ackerknecht, 'Beiträge', 101.

51 Ackerknecht, 'Beiträge', 89–93; Virchow, *Letters*, 59 (24/7/1845); Claudia Huerkamp, 'Ärzte und Professionalisierung in Deutschland', *Geschichte und Gesellschaft* 6 (1980): 357. For a more detailed discussion of the demographics of the profession, see *idem, Der Aufstieg der Ärzte im 19. Jahrhundert* (Göttingen: Vandenhoeck & Ruprecht, 1985), 50–52.

52 See the remarks of county-surgeon Bauer: "We want above all things a subsistence corresponding to our achievements and knowledge", quoted in Posner, 'Zur Geschichte des ärztlichen Vereinswesens', 1230.

53 *MR* 23 (8/12/1848): 158.

54 Riedel, 'Polizeiliche Knechtung des Ärztlichen Standes', *MR* 33 (16/2/1849): 197.

55 Finkenrath, *Medizinalreform*, 3–11; Huerkamp, 'Ärzte', 351–4; Ackerknecht, 'Beiträge', 92, 113.

56   Huerkamp, 'Ärzte', 357.

57   See, for example, Virchow, 'Der Staat und die Aerzte', *MR* 40 (6/4/1849): 225, draft for medical reform from Saxony, paragraph 2: "Midwives and all other medical personnel are wards of the medical [*Ärztlichen*] community and are without any franchise."

58   F Loffler, 'Ueber medicinische Pfuscherei und Polizei', *MR* 12 (22/9/1848): 79–80.

59   Virchow, 'Der Staat und die Aerzte', *MR* 37 (16/3/1848): 213–14 and 38 (23/3/ 1849): 217–18.

60   See, for example, *MR* 39 (30/3/1849): 222.

61   Finkenrath, *Medizinalreform*, 41–4.

62   'Bericht über die Reform-Vorgänge', *MR* 6 (11/8/1848): 35; Virchow, 'Der Staat und die Aerzte', *MR* 39 (30/3/1849): 222 and 40 (6/4/1849): 225–7; Ackerknecht, 'Beiträge', 127; Leubuscher, 'Die Associationen der Aerzte', *MR* 28 (12/1/1849): 178–9.

63   Remak, *MR* 42 (20/4/1849): 236, speaking at the General-Versammlung Berliner Aerzte; Leubuscher, 'Die Associationen der Aerzte', *MR* 28 (12/1/1849): 178. Leubuscher actually used the word "Stand".

64   Virchow, 'Die Anstellung von Armen-Aerzten', *MR* 32 (9/2/1849): 193–4; *idem*, 'Der Staat und die Aerzte', *MR* 39 (20/3/1849): 221–3.

65   Virchow, 'Der Staat und die Aerzte', *MR* 41 (13/4/1849): 229–30.

66   Virchow, Letters, 85–90 (24/3/1848–2/5/1848) (incl. first and third quotations); *idem*, 'Die Lage der Medicinal-Reform', *MR* 27 (5/1/1849): 173 (incl. second quotation); *idem*, 'Die Epidemien von 1848', *Archiv für pathologische Anatomie und Physiologie und für klinische Medicin* 3 (1848): 5; *idem*, 'Das Medicinal-Ministerium', *MR* 4 (28/7/1848): 13; *idem*, 'Die Anstellung von Armenärzten', *MR* 30 (26/1/1849): 185–6 (for Virchow's political principles).

67   Finkenrath, *Medizinalreform*, 56; [Virchow], 'Personal-Nachrichten', *MR* (16/3/ 1849): 216 (for first quotation); *idem*, 'Der Armenarzt', *MR* 18 (3/11/1848): 125 Virchow writes "who could wonder why democracy and socialism are nowhere stronger than among doctors? why everywhere doctors stand on the far left, sometimes at the head of the movement?"

68   'Rückblick', *MR* 11 (15/9/1848): 69.

69   Virchow, 'Der Staat und die Aerzte', *MR* 39 (30/3/1849): 222–3 and 40 (6/4/ 1849): 225–7; *MR* 6 (11/8/1848): 35 and 9 (1/9/1848): 59. Sometimes these drafts (such as the Berlin and Merseburg ones) made the connection between professional reform and general social politics explicit; at other times, demands for a democratic, rational and liberal organization of the medical profession implicitly established the connection to the level of high politics.

70   Salomon Neumann, *Die öffentliche Gesundheitspflege und das Eigenthum* (1847), excerpted in Hans-Ulrich Deppe and Michael Regus (eds), *Seminar: Medizin, Gesellschaft, Geschichte* (Frankfurt: Suhrkamp, 1975), 164–7.

71 Rudolf Leubuscher, 'Zur Reform der Sanitätspolizei', *MR* 3 (21/7/1848): 11–12; 8 (25/8/1848): 47–9.

72 Virchow, 'Was die "medicinische Reform" will', *MR* 1 (10/7/1848): 2.

73 Virchow, 'Der Armenarzt', *MR* 18 (3/11/1848): 125. Emphasis added.

74 Virchow, 'Die öffentliche Gesundheitspflege', *MR* 5 (4/8/1848): 21; *idem*, 'Report on the Typhus Epidemic', 313.

75 Virchow, 'Die öffentliche Gesundheitspflege', *MR* 8 (25/8/1848): 45; *idem*, 'Der Armenarzt', *MR* 18 (3/11/1848): 126; *idem*, 'Die Epidemien von 1848', 3–5.

76 Virchow, 'Die öffentliche Gesundheitspflege', *MR* 5 (4/8/1848): 21–2; 7 (18/8/1848): 37; *idem*, 'Der Staat und die Aerzte', *MR* 39 (30/3/1849): 221.

77 Virchow, 'Der Staat und die Aerzte', *MR* 39 (30/3/1849): 221.

78 Virchow, 'Die Epidemien von 1848', 7.

79 *MR* 6 (11/8/1848): 35; Virchow, 'Der Staat und die Aerzte', *MR* 40 (6/4/1849): 225–7.

80 Virchow, 'Der Staat und die Aerzte', *MR* 37 (16/3/1849): 213.

81 Evidence for this paragraph: Virchow, 'Der Armenarzt', *MR* 18 (3/11/1848): 125–7; *idem*, 'Die Anstellung von Armen-Aerzten', *MR* 30 (26/1/1849): 185–7; 31 (2/2/1849): 189–90; 32 (9/2/1849): 193–4; 34 (23/2/1849): 202–3.

82 See, for example, *MR* 4 (28/7/1848): 14 and *passim*.

83 *MR* Extrablatt to 2 (19/7/1849): 1.

84 Virchow, 'Der medicinische Congress', *MR* 17 (27/10/1848): 117.

85 'An die preussischen Aerzte', *MR* 6 (11/8/1848): 30–31.

86 Posner, 'Zur Geschichte des ärztlichen Vereinswesens', 1231.

87 *MR* 7 (18/8/1848): 41.

88 Virchow, 'Die Lage der Medicinal-Reform', *MR* 27 (5/1/1849): 173.

89 *MR* 38 (23/3/1849): 219, 238; Graf, *Das ärztliche Vereinswesen*, 14.

90 [Virchow], 'Die Enthüllungen über den ärztlichen Congress', *MR* 46 (18/5/1849): 249–50; 47 (25/5/1849): 253–4; 48 (1/6/1849): 257–8. On page 254, Virchow writes that "in the course of the last five months we stand for the second time on the threshold of a medical congress ... When this point is reached a third time, who will steer the ship of state through the breakers? Will we then have to call out: '*Zwischen Lipp' und Kelchesrand / Schwebt der düstern Mächte Hand*'?"

91 *MR* 39 (30/3/1849): 224.

92 Virchow, 'Die medicinische Verwaltung', *MR* 49 (8/6/1849): 262.

93 Evidence for this paragraph from: *MR* 42 (20/4/1849): 236; Finkenrath, *Medizinalreform*, 57; Virchow, 'Schluss', *MR* 52 (29/7/1849): 273–4; *idem*, *Letters*, 103 (6/4/1849), 106–12 (12/5–21/8/1849), 124 (20/12/1851).

94 Leubuscher, *MR* 5 (4/8/1848): 27.

95 Virchow, 'Die Lage der Medicinal-Reform', *MR* 27 (5/1/1849): 174.

96 Ackerknecht, 'Beiträge', 163.

97 Virchow, 'Die Lage der Medicinal-Reform', *MR* 27 (5/1/1849): 174.

98 Virchow, 'Radicalismus und Transaktion', *MR* 14 (6/10/1848): 94; *idem*, 'Der Armenarzt', *MR* 30 (26/1/1848): 185–6.

99 Virchow, 'Die Lage der Medizinal-Reform', *MR* 27 (5/1/1849): 174.

100 Virchow, 'Schluss', *MR* 52 (29/6/1849): 274.

101 Magistrat Berlin, *Bericht über die Gemeinde-Verwaltung* der Stadt Berlin in den Jahren 1861 bis 1876 (Berlin: Julius Sittenfeld, 1880), vol. 2, 125–8; John von Simson, *Kanalisation und Städtehygiene im 19. Jahrhundert* (Düsseldorf: Verein Deutscher Ingenieure, 1983), 91, 97; Fritz Langbein, 'Der Werdegang der Berliner Stadtentwässerung', in Hermann Hahn and Fritz Langbein (eds), *Fünfzig Jahre Berliner Stadtentwässerung, 1878–1928* (Berlin: Metzner, 1928), 17–19.

102 A E Silk, *A Report on the Drainage and Sewerage System of the City of Berlin* (Calcutta: Bengal Secretariat Press, 1894), 1. See also, for example, James Pollard, *A Study in Municipal Government. The Corporation of Berlin* (Edinburgh: Wm Blackwood & Sons, 1894), ch. 3; William Harbutt Dawson, *Municipal Life and Government in Germany* (London: Longmans, Green, and Co., 1914), 199. As these references suggest, the English, who had been pioneers in sewage treatment, were among the most fervent admirers of Berlin's system.

103 Isidor Kastan, *Berlin wie es war* (Berlin: Rudolf Mosse, 1919), 19. See also Pollard, *Corporation of Berlin*, 34: "For the beneficent changes that have been brought about in the sanitation of the city no man is so much entitled to public gratitude as Professor Virchow. He is one of the most industrious of the world's workers."

104 James J Sheehan, 'Liberalism and the City in Nineteenth-Century Germany', *Past and Present* 51 (1971): 116–23.

105 The Stein reforms granted most Prussian cities limited rights of self-government through an elected representative council; government-appointed administrative councillors, headed by a mayor, supervised the actual town government, however. The reforms were undertaken during the Napoleonic period, when Prussia recognized the need for local institutions of self-government. It should also be emphasized that Stein did not so much create these institutions as give them legal form and encourage their further development. Self-government had in fact existed in Germany since medieval times. Berlin, being a royal city (Residenzstadt), had not enjoyed these medieval traditions and therefore stood to gain that much more from Stein's reforms. See Heinrich Heffter, *Die deutsche Selbstverwaltung* (Stuttgart: K.F. Koehler, 1950), 92–6; and Sheehan, 'Liberalism and the City', 118.

106 Magistrat, *Gemeinde-Verwaltung*, vol. 2, 129.

107 Dieter Langewiesche, *Liberalismus in Deutschland* (Frankfurt: Suhrkamp, 1988), 202–3; Brian Ladd, *Urban Planning and Civic Order in Germany, 1860–1914* (Cambridge: Harvard University Press, 1990), 7–35.

108 Rudolf Virchow, 'General Report on the Findings of the Municipal Mixed Committee for the Investigation of Problems Relating to Canalization and

Removal of Wastes', *CEPHE*, trans. L J Rather (Canton, Mass: Watson Publishing International, 1985), vol. 2, 327.

109 Sheehan, 'Liberalism and the City', 120–21; Ladd, *Urban Planning*, 18–20.

110 According to an inequitable voting system, the wealthiest 22 per cent of eligible voters in 1862 selected two-thirds of Berlin city councilmen. By 1876 this figure had dropped to 9.6 per cent, signalling even greater disparity of political influence for the well-to-do. See Magistrat, *Gemeinde-Verwaltung*, vol. 1, 68 and on this trend in general, Wolfgang Hofmann, 'Preußische Stadtverordneten-versammlungen als Repräsentativ-Organe', in Jürgen Reulecke (ed.), *Die deutsche Stadt im Industriezeitalter* (Wuppertal: Peter Hammer, 1978), 49–50.

111 Chaired by the mayor, the Magistrat ran day-to-day city administration and reserved the right to approve legislation passed by the city council, or *Stadtverordnetenversammlung*. Significantly, the term that the Magistrat used was *bürgerlicher Gemeinsinn*, which carries overtones of a more social character. The word *bürgerlich* can mean either "civic" or "bourgeois". Citation from Magistrat, *Gemeinde-Verwaltung*, vol. 1, 16–17.

112 Magistrat, *Gemeinde-Verwaltung*, vol. 1, vii–viii.

113 Magistrat, *Gemeinde-Verwaltung*, vol. 2, 110–11. The idea of reforming the system of human waste removal through carts and pits was not yet an issue. On Crelle and Baeyer, see Simson, *Kanalisation und Städtehygiene*, 92–6; Langbein, 'Werdegang', 20–23.

114 Magistrat, *Gemeinde-Verwaltung*, vol. 2, 112.

115 Ibid., 119–20.

116 Ibid., 127.

117 Eduard Wiebe, *Über die Reinigung und Entwässerung Berlins* (Berlin: Ernst and Korn, 1861), vol. 1, 33, 57, 145, 210–17; vol. 2, 136, 182.

118 The estate-owners were not in fact actually obtaining human fertilizer at this time, but instead advocated creating a new system of cart-removal designed around sewage harvesting. This semblance of concern for sewerage reform actually made the agriculturalists appear less self-interested than they actually were.

119 Justus von Liebig, *Die Chemie in ihrer Anwendung auf Agricultur und Physiologie* (Braunschweig: Friedrich Vieweg, 1865), vol. 1, 134–56.

120 Virchow papers 2598 #34, Liebig quoted in the *National-Zeitung*, zweites Beiblatt, 19 Nov. 1872.

121 'Kritische Besprechungen', *DVföG* 3 (1871): 297–9; Virchow papers 2598 #34 *National-Zeitung* 19 Nov. 1872; *Reinigung und Entwässerung Berlins. Einleitende Verhandlungen und Berichte über mehrere auf Veranlassung des Magistrats der Königlichen Haupt- und Residenzstadt Berlin angestellte Versuche und Untersuchungen* (Berlin: August Hirschwald, 1870), 15–18, 30–31, 34–5, 37–46, 114–15 and *passim*. There were many other technical issues discussed that do not merit inclusion in the narrative.

122 C Skrzeczka, *Generalbericht über das Medizinal- und Sanitätswesen der Stadt Berlin* (Berlin: A W Hahns, 1882), 83, 86 (includes quotation); Langbein, 'Werdegang', 28.

123 'Einleitende Verhandlungen', *Reinigung und Entwässerung Berlins*, 14–17, 28–9, 30 (commission sittings from 1862–5) on Spott, Thorwirth, Veitmeyer, von Unruh (who was also a prominent liberal parliamentarian), and others. Also see Petra Tiarks-Jungk, 'Rudolf Virchows Beiträge zur öffentlichen Gesundheitspflege in Berlin' (Med. Diss., University of Gießen, 1984), 96–7.

124 'Vorlage des Magistrats vom 15 Mai 1866' and 'Bericht der Referenten der Stadtverordneten-Versammlung vom 17 November 1866', *Reinigung und Entwässerung Berlins*, 88–108 and 108–18, respectively. Virchow himself signed the council's list of questions.

125 *Reinigung und Entwässerung Berlins*, 123–31.

126 Virchow, 'Expert Opinion on the Most Effective Method for Disposing of Human Wastes in Berlin', *CEPHE*, vol. 2, 193.

127 On Pettenkofer and his ideas see Evans, *Death in Hamburg*, 237–43.

128 Virchow, 'Canalization or Removal?', *CEPHE*, vol. 2, 150ff. for Virchow's restatement and critique of Pettenkofer's groundwater theory. Virchow was at one time involved in a scientific controversy with Pettenkofer, but this dispute mainly centred on technicalities and not the broad outlines of Pettenkofer's theory. Virchow also objected to Pettenkofer's dogmatism and advocated a more pluralistic approach towards science (see below).

129 Virchow, 'General Report', 286–98.

130 Ibid., 301–20.

131 Ibid., 304.

132 Ibid., 236–46. Though Virchow admonished his readers to be "cautious in using mortality data in support of canalization", he none the less concluded that "precisely where infant morality had been highest [in England], the greatest decrease took place after sanitation was effected".

133 Virchow, 'Expert Opinion', 197–8.

134 Virchow, 'Canalization or Removal?', 221.

135 Virchow, 'General Report', 270.

136 Virchow, 'Expert Opinion', 214–15.

137 Ibid., 215.

138 Virchow, 'Expert Opinion', 215.

139 Ibid., 218. Emphasis in the original.

140 Virchow, 'Expert Opinion', 196; *idem*, 'General Report', 271–2.

141 Virchow, 'General Report', 271–2; *idem*, 'Expert Opinion', 215.

142 *Reinigung und Entwässerung Berlins*, vols. 2ff.

143 Ibid., 133–4.

144 Ingrid Thienel in *Neue Deutsche Biographie* (Berlin: Duncker and Humblot, 1953ff.), 280–81. The "Hobrecht plan" for Berlin was heavily criticized for its

reliance on "absolutist planning" instead of the freer growth offered by private development, but the connection between Hobrecht's statist/interventionist conception of urban planning and his attitude towards sanitary reform (see below) can only be pointed out here, and not analysed, for reasons of space. See Ladd, *Urban Planning*, 80–83; Simson, *Kanalisation und Städtehygiene*, 117–76; Jutta Lubowitzki, *Der Hobrechtplan. Probleme der Berliner Stadtentwicklung* (Berlin, 1990).

145 James Hobrecht, *Ueber öffentliche Gesundheitspflege und die Bildung eines Central-Amts für öffentliche Gesundheitspflege im Staate* (Stettin, 1868), quoted in Simson, *Kanalisation und Städtehygiene*, 117–18.

146 Hobrecht, *Die Canalisation von Berlin* (Berlin: Ernst & Korn, 1884), 4–55.

147 Proposals for a so-called *Mischkanalisation* competed with suggestions for a separated system of cart-removal for human wastes and canalization for other waters that enjoyed a brief heyday, but Hobrecht's plan proved feasible enough to include both forms of sewage in a general canalization.

148 'Die Rieselguter', *Die öffentliche Gesundheitspflege der Stadt Berlin* (Berlin: August Hirschwald, 1890), 297–312; Tiarks-Jungk, 'Rudolf Virchows Beiträge', 126–130.

149 Magistrat, *Gemeinde-Verwaltung*, vol. 2, 130; on the costs, see Hobrecht, 'Zur Canalisation von Berlin', *DVföG* 4 (1872): 646–8. In this article he estimates that homeowners would have to pay about 81 marks annually to join the system.

150 Magistrat, *Gemeinde-Verwaltung*, vol. 2, 131; Hobrecht, *Canalisation*, 1–2; for the final endorsement, see Virchow, 'General Report', 376.

151 'Taktik der Berliner Abfuhrmänner', *DVföG* 4 (1872), 656.

152 Virchow papers 2598 #36 *Deutsche Landwirthschaftliche Zeitung*, 8 Feb. 1873.

153 Virchow papers 2598 #35 *Annalen der Landwirthschaft in den Königlich-Preußischen Staaten*, 14 Dec. 1872; #3 ibid., 5 May 1869.

154 Virchow papers 2598 #23 *Volks-Zeitung*, 28 May 1872. On the financing of canalization see below.

155 Evidence for last two paragraphs: Virchow papers 2598 #1 'Der praktische Scharfblick' (also for first quotation); #22, 'Versammlung der Stadtbezirke 107–17'; #25, 'Zur Kanalisirung Berlins' (by 35 Bürger); #39, *Berliner Bürger-Zeitung*, 20 Feb. 1873 (for second quotation); #76, 'Aufruf an alle Mitbürger'. (also for third quotation); 2599 #25 'Bürgerversammlung der Schönhauser Allee'. With the exception of 2598 #1, which dates from 1866, the above-cited petitions date from 1872–3. Many of these petitions give the names and professions of the citizen action committee members, giving a clear impression of their bourgeois constituency. See also Magistrat, *Gemeinde-Verwaltung*, vol. 2, 130, which confirms the points of agreement of the citizenry.

156 Virchow papers 2599 #26, 'stenographischer Bericht der Stadtverordneten-versammlung', 3 Mar. 1873.

157 Magistrat, *Gemeinde-Verwaltung*, 134; Langbein, 'Werdegang', 31. The 3 March vote was 83 in favour, 19 against.

158 Magistrat, *Gemeinde-Verwaltung*, vol. 1, 9–10, 18–19; Pollard, *Corporation of Berlin*, 7–11. For a discussion of the relations between council and Magistrat, see Dawson, *Municipal Life*, 81–122.

159 Virchow papers 2595 #22 'Zur Kanalisirungsfrage: Beilage XVI zum Communalblatt', 15 May 1866.

160 Magistrat, *Gemeinde-Verwaltung*, vol. 2, 132–3.

161 *SBHA* 9 Feb. 1870, 2032 (Virchow).

162 The conservatism of the Magistrat, manifest here in its failure to work through truly democratic channels of government, is one instance of a more general phenomenon. Due to the influence the Prussian regime had over the appointment of administrative officials in city governments, National Liberals (moderates) tended to dominate the Magistrat (Forckenbeck, for instance, was mayor of Berlin at this time) while Progressives (left liberals, including Virchow) tended to dominate city councils. See Heffter, *Die deutsche Selbstverwaltung*, 616–19; Langewiesche, *Liberalismus in Deutschland*, 203–5. Anecdotal evidence of this smoldering leftism in city councils is given by a Berlin council petition that Virchow mentioned and supported in parliament, proposing the abrogation of the three-class voting system (a traditional favourite of moderates) in favour of universal and direct suffrage. See *SBHA* 3 Nov. 1869, 291–3 (Virchow).

163 Hobrecht, 'Zur Canalisation von Berlin', 641, 643.

164 Magistrat, *Gemeinde-Verwaltung*, vol. 2, 136; Virchow, 'General Report', 376–7.

165 Hobrecht, 'Zur Canalisation von Berlin', 644–5.

166 Magistrat, *Gemeinde-Verwaltung*, vol. 2, 136–7. This was endorsed by Virchow, 'General Report', 375.

167 Ladd, *Urban Planning*, 55.

168 *SBHA* 9 Feb. 1870, 2033; 9 Jan. 1872, 298–304 (Virchow).

169 Magistrat, *Gemeinde-Verwaltung*, vol. 2, 136–7, 394–8 (for text of the Polizei-Verordnung of 14 July 1874 and the Ortsstatut of 8 Sept. 1874). For further technical details, see Hobrecht, 'Die Kanalisation', in *Die öffentliche Gesundheitspflege*, 290–91.

170 Hobrecht, 'Zur Canalisation von Berlin', 644.

171 Virchow, 'Eröffnungs- und Begrüssungsrede des X. internationalen medicinischen Congresses', BKW 32 (1890): 722ff.

172 *SBHA* 9 Jan. 1872, 299 (Virchow).

173 Kastan, *Berlin wie es war*, 21.

174 Skrzeczka, *Generalbericht*, 86–9; Hobrecht, 'Die Kanalisation', 289.

175 Magistrat, *Gemeinde-Verwaltung*, vol. 2, 83–4, 121; Tiarks-Jungk, 'Rudolf Virchows Beiträge', 113; *SBHA* 28 Nov. 1873, 124–7 (Virchow); 'Die Rieselgüter', 297–312.

176 Virchow, 'Ueber Städtereinigung und die Verwendung der städtischen Unreinigkeiten', Separatabdruck from *DVföG* 15 (1883), 14.

177 Byron Boyd, 'Rudolf Virchow. The Scientist as Citizen' (PhD Diss., University of North Carolina, 1981), 229.

178 Sheehan, 'Liberalism and the City', 135.

179 *SBHA* 5 Dec. 1883, 202 (Virchow).

180 Kaiserliches Gesundheitsamt, *Das Deutsche Reich in gesundheitlicher und demographischer Beziehung* (Berlin: Puttkammer & Mühlbrecht, 1907), 281.

181 M Pistor, *Deutsches Gesundheitswesen* (Berlin: Julius Springer, 1890), 138.

182 *SBR* 20–21 Nov. 1891, 2960–62, 2970–80, 2990; 15 Mar. 1892, 4752–5; *SBHA* 16 Mar. 1892, 956–9 (Virchow).

183 *SBR* 31 May 1883, 2696. The final vote was 216 in favour, 99 opposed. It is conceivable that personal circumstances kept Virchow from debating the bill. By the 1880s, his anthropological expeditions took him out of Berlin quite frequently, so it is possible that he was not available before the 31st to participate in the debate. But in early 1883 he had just returned from a trip to the Caucasus, so it is unlikely that he would have turned around so quickly and made another trip that year. Available sources do not yield a definitive conclusion. In any case, it is bizarre that Virchow never took the opportunity (even after the fact) to make his opinion on sickness insurance officially known.

184 A reprint of the law's text is found in D Wiener, *Handbuch der Medizinal-Gesetzgebung des deutschen Reichs und seiner Einzelstaaten* (Stuttgart: Ferdinand Enke, 1883), first supplement to vol. 1, 7–34.

185 In its original incarnation, sickness insurance targeted mainly those workers in the most politically volatile trades – mining, industry, etc. – and was only later extended to agricultural labourers and domestic servants.

186 Quoted in William Harbutt Dawson, *Bismarck and State Socialism* (London: Swan Sonnenschein, 1890), 111. Emphasis added.

187 Jürgen Tampke, 'Bismarck's Social Legislation: a Genuine Breakthrough?', in W J Mommsen and Wolfgang Mock (eds), *The Emergence of the Welfare State in Britain and Germany* (London: Croom Helm, 1981), 71. The quotation is from Wolfgang Treue.

188 Hans-Ulrich Wehler, *The German Empire*, trans. Kim Traynor (Leamington Spa: Berg, 1985), 132–7. The term "carrot and stick" (*Brot und Peitsche*) is from Wehler's book. The phrases "sugar coating" and "bitter pill" come from Geoff Eley, 'Possibilities of Reform in Britain and Germany', in David Blackbourn and Geoff Eley, *The Peculiarites of German History* (Oxford: Oxford University Press, 1984), 100, in which Eley critiques Wehler's view.

189 Tampke, 'Bismarck's Social Legislation', 71–82.

190 Dieter Langewiesche, *Liberalismus in Deutschland* (Frankfurt: Suhrkamp, 1988), 195–8.

191 There were liberals who concerned themselves actively with social policy, including Lujo Brentano, Gustav Schmoller, and other members of the *Verein für Sozialpolitik*, for example. But during the 1870s and 1880s, many of these liberal social scientists – despite their moderate and sometimes monarchist inclinations – were regarded suspiciously by their more mainstream colleagues. See ch. 5 for more on this.

192 It should be clear that my concept of conservative state interventionism mixes Wehler's and Tampke's ideas on social policy. In particular, it emphasizes both manipulation (Wehler) and neglect (Tampke) as parts of a single conservative outlook centred around state preservation.

193 A further note: perhaps due to this methodological difficulty, the history of Virchow's parliamentary health politics has until recently been totally neglected in the literature. Only with the aid of Anja Thybusch, 'Rudolf Virchow. Parlamentarische Tätigkeit und Gesundheitspolitik in Reichstag und preussischem Abgeordnetenhaus' (Med. Diss., University of Kiel, 1989), which catalogues references to all of Virchow's speeches, have I been able to ensure thoroughness in my approach. A complete edition of Virchow's work, including his parliamentary speeches and political papers, is in the process of being published, but as of this writing only volumes 30–36, covering his years in the Prussian legislature from 1861 to 1887, have appeared. See Virchow's *Sämtliche Werke in 71 Bänden*, ed. Christian Andree (Berlin: Blackwell Wissenschafts-Verlag, 1992ff.).

194 *Deutsche Vierteljahrsschrift für öffentliche Gesundheitspflege*, abbreviated in this study as *DVföG*.

195 Max von Pettenkofer, 'The Value of Health to a City' (1873), *Bulletin of the History of Medicine* 10 (1941), trans. Henry Sigerist, 492.

196 Carl Reclam, 'Die heutige Gesundheitspflege und ihre Aufgaben', *DVföG* 1 (1869): 1.

197 *SBHA* 22 Feb. 1868, 1833–4; 14 Jan. 1868, 847 (Virchow) (in order of quotation). In this Virchow proved his willingness to accommodate his ideas to the broader philosophy of public health, much as he did in canalization, when he also mixed ethical and economic appeals.

198 The term "beachhead" comes from James Sheehan, 'Liberalism and the City in Nineteenth-Century Germany', *Past and Present* 51 (1971): 137; on the depoliticization of public health, see Brian Ladd, *Urban Planning and Civic Order in Germany, 1860–1914* (Cambridge: Harvard University Press, 1990), 73–6.

199 Paul Boerner (ed.), *Bericht über die Allgemeine deutsche Ausstellung auf dem Gebiete der Hygiene und des Rettungswesens* (Breslau: Schottlaender Verlag, 1885), 3 vols.

200 Gertrud Kroeger, *The Concept of Social Medicine ... in Germany* (Chicago: Julius Rosenwald, 1937), 23–31; George Rosen, 'What is Social Medicine?', *Bulletin of the History of Medicine* 21 (1947): 709–16.

201 A film from the Nazi era attests both to this popular image and to Koch's appeal to conservative ideologues. Hans Steinhoff's *Robert Koch: Bekämpfer des Todes* (1939) depicts Koch as a crusading scientist and caricatures Virchow as a doddering fool. See Arnold Bauer, *Rudolf Virchow* (Berlin: Stapp, 1982), 78, 80. For scholarly literature on this subject, see Hans-Ulrich Lammel, 'Virchow contra Koch?', *Zeitschrift für die gesamte Hygiene* 28 (1982): 206–10; Manfred Stürzbecher, 'Rudolf Virchow und die kommunale Gesundheitspolitik in Berlin', *Verhandlungen der Deutschen Gesellschaft für Pathologie* 68 (1984): xxxviii.

202 *SBHA* 6 Feb 1897, 814–16; 5 Mar. 1889, 800–803, 810–11; *SBR* 13 May 1884, 573 (for quotation) (Virchow). In the second speech cited, Virchow proved he had no animosity towards Koch. In advocating a scientific deputation to be headed by Koch to study cholera in Egypt, Virchow stressed his achievement and, through his tone, made it clear that he only wished to gently prod his audience to consider alternatives to Koch's theory.

203 Evans, *Death in Hamburg*, 266. See also his general discussion of Koch and conservatism, 264–72.

204 Part of the more general 'Reichs-Gesetz, betr. den Verkehr mit Nahrungsmitteln, Genußmitteln und Gebrauchsgegenständen', 14 May 1879, reprinted Wiener, *Medizinal-Gesetzgebung*, vol. 1, 114–59. See also Pistor, *Deutsches Gesundheitswesen*, 100–117. On this law and others mentioned here, see O Dammer, *Handwörterbuch der Gesundheitspflege* (Stuttgart: Ferdinand Enke, 1891), esp. 287–91, article on 'Gesundheitspflege'.

205 'Reichs-Impfgesetz', 8 Apr. 1874, reprinted in Wiener, *Medizinal-Gesetzgebung*, vol. 1, 83–9. See also Claudia Huerkamp, 'The History of Smallpox Vaccination in Germany: A First Step in the Medicalization of the German Public', *Journal of Contemporary History* 20 (1985): 617–35, esp. 620–21 on the state's rationales.

206 'Bekämpfung der Infektionskrankheiten', esp. 'Massnahmen gegen die Cholera', 'Massnahmen, betreffend ärztliche Kontrolle der Seeschiffe', 'Massnahmen, betreffend Desinfektion der Schiffe und der Eisenbahnviehwagen', in Pistor, *Deutsches Gesundheitswesen*, 50–87.

207 *SBR* 13 May 1884, 572 (Virchow).

208 Virchow, 'Offering for Sale of Trichinous Meat', *CEPHE*, trans. L J Rather, vol. 2, 488, 489–90; Petra Tiarks-Jungk, 'Rudolf Virchows Beiträge', 84–9.

209 *SBHA* 5 Apr. 1875, 959–60 (for quotation); 3 Mar. 1866, 1218–21 (Virchow).

210 *SBHA* 22 Feb. 1868, 1830–5 (first quotation); 9 Feb. 1875, 144–9 (second quotation); 14 Jan. 1868, 844–7, 858–60; 4 July 1893, 2530–33; 12 Jan. 1880, 852–9, 871 (Virchow).

211 Pistor, *Deutsches Gesundheitswesen*, 4–11.

212 *SBR* 13 May 1884, 572–4; 2 Dec. 1881, 172–4; *SBHA* 17 Mar. 1898, 1570–73 (Virchow).

213 *SBHA* 25 June 1895, 2465–8 (Virchow).

214 *SBHA* 25 June 1895, 2465–8; 13 Mar. 1901, Spalte 3313–19; 7 Mar. 1898, 1223–6; 7 May 1897, 2532–6 (Virchow).

215 *SBHA* 17 Mar. 1898, 1570–73; 13 Mar. 1901, Spalte 3313–19; 25 June 1895, 2465–8 (Virchow). Military medicine was another example. Virchow implied that both of these areas received special attention for political reasons – veterinary medicine for the big agriculturalists, the military for obvious reasons.

216 *SBHA* 27 Jan. 1868, 1173–8 (Virchow). For his proposal, see *SBHA* Antrag #204 for 1867 session.

217 Goltdammer, 'Medizinalwesen', in Dammer, *Handwörterbuch der Gesundheitspflege*, 556–64; Pistor, *Deutsches Gesundheitswesen*, 163; Albert Guttstadt, *Deutschlands Gesundheitswesen* (Leipzig: Georg Thieme, 1890), 47–50.

218 See Pistor, *Deutsches Gesundheitswesen*, 155–63, on the functions of the Provinzial-Medizinal-Kollegien and the Regierungs-Medizinal-Räthe.

219 Huerkamp, *Der Aufstieg der Ärzte im 19. Jahrhundert* (Göttingen: Vandenhoeck & Ruprecht, 1985), 167–77; Pistor, *Deutsches Gesundheitswesen*, 152–63. Local health officials had the responsibility both for overseeing medical police affairs and matters concerned with the professional licensing and examination of private physicians, which will be discussed below.

220 In 1816 *Kreisphysiker* were paid about 200 Taler (600 Mark) and in 1872 still only 300 Taler (900 Mark). Attempts to improve their compensation in 1902–4 were ineffective, and they remained poorly paid. See Huerkamp, *Aufstieg*, 168, 171, 174.

221 *SBHA* 28 Feb. 1873, 1285–8 (for quotation); 13 Feb. 1872, 758–60, 762–4; 8 Feb. 1878, 1705–6 (Virchow). Due to their meagre salaries, many *Kreisärzte* did in fact turn to private practice for supplemental income. See Huerkamp, *Aufstieg*, 171.

222 See Gesetz-Entwurf promulgated on 1 April 1872 (*SBHA* Drucksache #143).

223 See, for example, A Gottstein, 'Die staatliche Organisation des Sanitätswesens', in George Stockhausen (ed.), *Das Deutsche Jahrhundert in Einzelschriften* (Berlin: F Schneider, 1902), vol. 2, 236–51.

224 Huerkamp, 'Smallpox Vaccination', 621–4, 631.

225 Huerkamp, *Aufstieg*, 194–240 (also see below).

226 For the 1827 statistic: Huerkamp, 'Ärzte und Professionalisierung in Deutschland', *Geschichte und Gesellschaft* 6 (1980): 361; for 1887, Pistor, *Deutsches Gesundheitswesen*, 40–41.

227 See Paul Starr, *The Social Transformation of American Medicine* (New York: Basic Books, 1982). On Virchow's particular praise for American freedoms for the medical profession, see *SBR* 15 Mar. 1892, 4753 (Virchow).

228 Huerkamp, 'Ärzte', 359–60.

229 H Bläsner, 'Die standespolitischen Diskussionen in der Berliner Medizinischen Gesellschaft', cited in Huerkamp, 'Ärzte', 363–4.

230 On the proceedings of the Berlin Medical Society and Virchow's role in them, see *BKW* 6 (1869): 147, 156, 535. On Loewe's speech, *SBR* 4 Apr. 1869, 303–5 (Loewe).

231 Pistor, *Deutsches Gesundheitswesen*, 11–13.

232 Arthur Gabriel, *Die staatliche Organisation des Deutschen Aerztestandes* (Berlin: Adler-Verlag, 1919), 28–9, 55; Huerkamp, 'Ärzte', 366–7.

233 'Grundzüge einer deutschen Ärzteordnung', reprinted in Eduard Graf, *Das ärztliche Vereinswesen in Deutschland und der deutsche Ärztevereinsbund* (Leipzig: F C W Vogel, 1890), 43–5.

234 *SBHA* 9 Feb. 1884, 1350 (Virchow) (both quotations).

235 *SBHA* 16 Mar. 1893, 956–9; 9 Feb. 1884, 1351 (Virchow).

236 *SBHA* 16 Mar. 1886, 1218–21 (Virchow).

237 'Staatlich anerkannte Standesvertretung', 27 May 1887, reprinted in Guttstadt, *Deutschlands Gesundheitswesen*, 51–60. See Graf, *Das ärztliche Vereinswesen*, 36ff.; Gabriel, *Die staatilche Organisation*, 55–8, 78–81.

238 Guttstadt, *Deutschlands Gesundheitswesen*, 52–3.

239 *SBHA* 9 Feb. 1884, 1351; 4 Feb. 1899, 337 (Virchow).

240 Guttstadt, *Deutschlands Gesundheitswesen*, 52.

241 Huerkamp, *Aufstieg*, 265–7.

242 Gabriel, *Die staatliche Organisation*, 105–9.

243 *SBHA* 16 Mar. 1892, 956–9 (Virchow).

244 Huerkamp, 'Ärzte', 378; Gabriel, *Die staatliche Organisation*, 126. Gabriel offers an excrutiating, blow-by-blow account of this debate.

245 Gabriel, *Die staatliche Organisation*, 138–43; Huerkamp, *Aufstieg*, 265–72.

246 *SBHA* 4 Feb. 1899, 337–41 (Virchow).

247 Gerd Göckenjan, *Kurieren und Staat machen. Gesundheit und Medizin in der bürgerlichen Welt* (Frankfurt: Suhrkamp, 1985), 363–72.

248 Huerkamp, *Aufstieg*, 279ff.; *idem*, 'Ärzte', 375–7.

249 *SBR* 20 Nov. 1891, 2960–62; 15 Mar. 1892, 4752–5 (Virchow).

250 Reinhard Spree, *Health and Social Class in Imperial Germany*, Stuart McKinnon-Evans (trans.) (Oxford: Berg, 1988), 171–2.

251 *SBR* Anlagen, 1890–92 session, 2858 (Eberty and Virchow). The proposal did allow for treatment by non-certified doctors who none the less had some form of "technical" training, but only in the case of "urgent danger".

252 *SBR* 15 Mar. 1892, 4753 (Virchow).

253 Spree, *Health and Social Class*, 172.

254 Ralf Dahrendorf, *Society and Democracy in Germany* (New York: W.W. Norton, 1967), esp. 14, 29; also in this vein, Fritz Stern, *The Failure of Illiberalism: Essays on the Political Culture of Modern Germany* (New York: Knopf, 1972).

255 Theodore Hamerow, *Restoration, Revolution, Reaction* (Princeton: Princeton University Press, 1958), 137–55 (on artisans), 156–72 (on peasants), 173–95 (on the fall of liberalism).

256 James Sheehan, *German Liberalism in the Nineteenth Century* (Chicago: University of Chicago Press, 1978), esp. 95–107. See also Eugene Anderson, *Social and Political Conflict in Prussia, 1858–1864* (Lincoln, Neb.: University of Nebraska Press, 1954); Hamerow, *The Social Foundations of German Unification, 1858–1871, Ideas and Institutions* (Princeton: Princeton University Press, 1969) and the second volume of this work, *Struggles and Accomplishments* (1972).

257 Otto Pflanze, *Bismarck and the Development of Germany* (Princeton: Princeton University Press, 1963); Leonard Krieger, *The German Idea of Freedom: History of a Political Tradition* (Boston: Beacon Press, 1957).

258 Pflanze, *Bismarck*, vol. 1, 326.

259 Hans-Ulrich Wehler, *The German Empire*, Kim Traynor (trans.) (Oxford: Berg, 1985), 24–6, 55 and *passim*.

260 David Blackbourn and Geoff Eley, *The Peculiarities of German History: Bourgeois Society and Politics in Nineteenth-Century Germany* (Oxford: Oxford University Press, 1984), 56, 75.

261 See Konrad Jarausch and Larry Eugene Jones (eds), *In Search of a Liberal Germany: Studies in the History of German Liberalism from 1789 to the Present* (New York: Berg, 1990); and Dieter Langewiesche, *Liberalismus in Deutschland* (Frankfurt: Suhrkamp, 1988), perhaps best general synthesis to explore liberalism's strengths and weaknesses, locally and nationally, in culture and society as well as in politics.

262 See David Blackbourn and Richard J Evans (eds), *The German Bourgeoisie* (London: Routledge, 1991). In the realm of medical history, for example, Paul Weindling ties the professionalization of German doctors – as an up-and-coming bourgeois group – both to the eclipse of liberalism and to the concomitant rise of eugenic and racial ideologies allowing them to assert their competence, as experts in biological science, over the domain of the "social". See his contribution to *The German Bourgeoisie*, 'Bourgeois Values, Doctors, and the State: the Professionalization of Medicine in Germany, 1848–1933', 198–223, as well as his monograph, *Health, Race, and German Politics between National Unification and Nazism, 1870–1945* (Cambridge: Cambridge University Press, 1989).

263 This direction has been championed by Eley himself in his 'Liberalism, Europe, and the Bourgeoisie 1860–1914', in Blackbourn and Evans, *The German Bourgeoisie*, 293–317.

264 Wolfgang Mommsen's controversial monograph on Max Weber's nationalistic liberalism, *Max Weber and German Politics 1890–1920* (Chicago: University of Chicago Press, 1984 [1974, 1959]), stands out in this respect. There is also a copious literature on Weber's colleague Friedrich Naumann, founder of the liberal-reformist *National-Sozialer Verein* (whose progressive ideology should, however, not be confused with National Socialism). See Peter Theiner, *Sozialer Liberalismus und deutsche Weltpolitik: Friedrich Naumann im Wilhelminischen Deutschland (1860–1919)* (Baden-Baden: Nomos, 1983); Dieter Düding,

Der National-Sozialer Verein, 1896–1903. Der gescheiterte Versuch einer parteipolitischen Synthese von Nationalismus, Sozialismus und Liberalismus (München: R Oldenbourg, 1972). Other studies of social liberalism in this period include Klaus Holl and Günther Trautmann (eds.), *Sozialer Liberalismus* (Göttingen: Vandenhoeck & Ruprecht, 1986); and Dieter Lindenlaub, *Richtungskämpfe im Verein für Sozialpolitik. Wissenschaft und Sozialpolitik im Kaiserreich vornehmlich vom Beginn des Neuen Kurses bis zum Ausbruch des Ersten Weltkrieges, 1890–1914* (Wiesbaden: Steiner, 1967).

265 In addition to the works of William Harbutt Dawson and other admirers of German government cited in ch. 3 above, see the recently published work by Daniel T Rodgers, *Atlantic Crossings: Social Politics in a Progressive Age* (Cambridge: Harvard University Press, 1998), and the earlier intellectual history by James Kloppenberg, *Uncertain Victory. Social Democracy and Progressivism in European and American Thought* (Oxford: Oxford University Press, 1986). Also, Rüdiger vom Bruch (ed.), *Weder Kommunismus noch Kapitalismus. Bürgerliche Sozialreform in Deutschland vom Vormärz bis zur Ära Adenauer* (München: C H Beck, 1985).

Bibliography

Primary Sources

UNPUBLISHED MATERIALS

Nachlaß Rudolf Virchow. Zentrales Archiv, Akademie der Wissenschaften. Berlin. (Virchow papers)

COLLECTED WORKS

Virchow, Rudolf. *Collected Essays on Public Health and Epidemiology* (*CEPHE*). 2 volumes. Edited and translated by L J Rather. Canton, Mass.: Watson Publishing International, 1985.

Works cited in the text:

'Canalization or Removal?', vol. 2, 221–66.
'Expert Opinion on the Most Effective Method of Disposing of Human Wastes in Berlin', vol. 2, 193–220.
'General Report on the Findings of the Municipal Mixed Committee for the Investigation of Problems Relating to Canalization and Removal of Wastes', vol. 2, 267–401.
'Offering for Sale of Trichinous Meat', vol. 2, 488–90.
'Report on the Typhus Epidemic in Upper Silesia', vol. 1, 205–319.

———. *Letters to His Parents, 1839 to 1864*. Translated by L J Rather. Canton, Mass.: Watson Publishing International, 1990.

——— and R Leubuscher, eds. *Die medicinische Reform* (*MR*). 52 volumes. Collected by Christa Kirsten and Kurt Zeisler. Berlin: Akademie-Verlag, 1983.

Works in MR *by Virchow cited in the text:*

'Das Medizinal-Ministerium', 9–11, 13–16.
'Der Armenarzt', 125–7.
'Der medicinische Congress', 117–19.
'Der Staat und die Aerzte', 213–15, 217–18, 221–3, 225–7, 229–30.
  'Die Anstellung von Armen-Aerzten', 185–7, 189–90, 193–4, 202–203.
  'Die Enthüllungen über den ärztlichen Congress', 249–50, 253–4, 257–8.

Bibliography

'Die Lage der Medicinal-Reform', 173–4.
'Die medicinische Verwaltung', 261–2.
'Die öffentliche Gesundheitspflege', 21–2, 37–40, 45–7, 53–6.
'Radikalismus und Transaktion', 93-95.
'Schluss', 273–4.
'Was die "medicinische Reform" will', 1–2.

Works in MR *by other authors cited in the text:*

Leubuscher, Rudolf. 'Die Associationen der Aerzte', 178–9.
——. 'Zur Reform der Sanitätspolizei', 11–12, 47–9.
Riedel. 'Polizeiliche Knechtung des ärztlichen Standes', 197.
Loffler, F. 'Ueber medicinische Pfuscherei und Polizei', 79–80.

——. *Rudolf Virchow und die deutschen Naturforscherversammlungen.* Edited by Karl Sudhoff. Leipzig, 1922.

Parliamentary proceedings

Stenographische Berichte über die Verhandlungen des Landtages, Haus der Abgeordneten (SBHA)

Stenographische Berichte über die Verhandlungen des Reichstags (SBR)

See also the work by Anja Thybusch (below), which catalogues Virchow's parliamentary speeches.

Other sources

'Actenstücke über die Entwässerung Berlins, der Stadtverordnetenversammlung vorgelegt'. *DVföG* 4 (1872): 456–86.
Berlin, Magistrat. *Bericht über die Gemeinde-Verwaltung der Stadt Berlin in den Jahren 1861 bis 1876.* 3 volumes. Berlin: Julius Sittenfeld, 1880.
Boerner, Paul. *Bericht über die Allgemeine deutsche Ausstellung auf dem Gebiete der Hygiene und des Rettungswesens.* 3 volumes. Breslau: Schottlaender Verlag, 1885.
——, ed. *Hygienischer Führer durch Berlin.* Berlin, 1882.
Dammer, O. *Handwörterbuch der Gesundheitspflege.* Stuttgart: Ferdinand Enke, 1891.
Dawson, William Harbutt. *Bismarck and State Socialism.* London: Swan Sonnenschein, 1890.
——. *Municipal Life and Government in Germany.* London: Longmans, Green, and Co., 1914.
'Die Canalisirungsfrage'. *DVföG* 4 (1872): 165–7.

Bibliography

Die öffentliche Gesundheitspflege der Stadt Berlin. Berlin: August Hirschwald, 1890.

Gabriel, Arthur. *Die staatliche Organisation des Deutschen Aerztestandes*. Berlin: Adler-Verlag, 1919.

Gesundheitsamt, Kaiserliches. *Das Deutsche Reich in gesundheitlicher und demographischer Beziehung*. Berlin: Puttkammer & Mühlbrecht, 1907.

Gottstein, A. 'Die staatliche Organisation des Sanitätswesens'. In George Stockhausen, ed. *Das Deutsche Jahrhundert in Einzelschriften*. 2 volumes. Berlin: F. Schneider, 1902.

Graf, Eduard. *Das ärztliche Vereinswesen in Deutschland und der deutsche Aerztevereinsbund*. Leipzig: F C W Vogel, 1890.

Guttstadt, Albert. *Deutschlands Gesundheitswesen*. Leipzig: Georg Thieme, 1890.

Hobrecht, James. *Die Canalisation von Berlin*. Berlin: Ernst and Korn, 1884.

———. 'Zur Canalisation von Berlin'. *DVföG* 4 (1872): 641–51.

Kastan, Isidor. *Berlin wie es war*. Berlin: Rudolf Mosse, 1919.

'Kritische Besprechungen'. *DVföG* 3 (1871): 297–9.

Liebig, Justus von. *Die Chemie in ihrer Anwendung auf Agricultur und Physiologie*. 2 volumes. Braunschweig: Friedrich Vieweg, 1865.

Neumann, Salomon. *Die öffentliche Gesundheitspflege und das Eigenthum* [1847]. Excerpted in Hans-Ulrich Deppe and Michael Regus (eds.), *Seminar: Medizin, Gesellschaft, Geschichte*. Frankfurt: Suhrkamp, 1975.

Pettenkofer, Max von. 'The Value of Health to a City'. Translated by Henry Sigerist. *Bulletin of the History of Medicine* 10 (1941): 487–503, 593–613.

Pistor, M. *Deutsches Gesundheitswesen*. Berlin: Julius Springer, 1890.

Pollard, James. *A Study in Municipal Government. The Corporation of Berlin*. Edinburgh: Wm. Blackwood & Sons, 1894.

Posner, C. 'Zur Geschichte des ärztlichen Vereinswesens in Berlin', *BKW* 30 (1893): 1230–31, 1257, 1271.

Reclam, Carl. 'Die heutige Gesundheitspflege und ihre Aufgaben'. *DVföG* 1 (1869): 1–4.

Reinigung und Entwässerung Berlins. Einleitende Verhandlungen und Berichte über mehrere auf Veranlassung des Magistrats der Königlichen Haupt- und Residenzstadt Berlin angestellte Versuche und Untersuchungen. 13 volumes. Berlin: August Hirschwald, 1870.

Silk, A E. *A Report on the Drainage and Sewerage System of the City of Berlin*. Calcutta: Bengal Secretariat Press, 1894.

Skzeczka, C. *Generalbericht über das Medizinal- und Sanitätswesen der Stadt Berlin*. Berlin: A W Hahns, 1882.

'Taktik der Berliner Abfuhrmnner'. *DVföG* 4 (1872): 656–7.

Virchow, Rudolf. *Die Anstalten der Stadt Berlin für die öffentliche Gesundheitspflege und den naturwissenschaftlichen Unterricht*. Berlin, 1890.

———. *Die Cellularpathologie*. 4th ed. Berlin: Hirschwald, 1871.

Bibliography

——. 'Die Epidemien von 1848'. *Archiv für pathologische Anatomie und Physiologie und für klinische Medicin* 3 (1848): 5–10.

——. 'Eröffnungs- und Begrüssungsrede des X. internationalen medicinischen Congresses'. *BKW* 32 (1890): 722ff.

——. *Die Freiheit der Wissenschaft im modernen Staat.* Berlin: Wiegandt, Hempel & Parey, 1877.

——. *Sämtliche Werke in 71 Bänden.* Edited by Christian Andree. Berlin: Blackwell Wissenschafts-Verlag, 1992ff.

——. 'Ueber Städtereinigung und die Verwendung der städtischen Unreinigkeiten'. Separatabdruck from *DVföG* 15 (1883): 1–21.

Wiebe, Eduard. *Über die Reinigung und Entwässerung Berlins.* Berlin: Ernst and Korn, 1861.

Wiener, David. *Handbuch der Medizinal-Gesetzgebung des Deutschen Reichs und seiner Einzelstaaten.* 4 volumes. Stuttgart: Ferdinand Enke, 1883.

Secondary works

Ackerknecht, Erwin. 'Beiträge zur Geschichte der Medizinalreform von 1848'. *Sudhoffs Archiv für Geschichte der Medizin* 25 (1932): 61–109, 113–83.

——. *Rudolf Virchow: Doctor, Statesman, Anthropologist.* New York: Arno Press, 1981 [1953].

Anderson, Eugene N. *The Social and Political Conflict in Prussia 1858–1864.* Lincoln: University of Nebraska Press, 1954.

Bauer, Arnold. *Rudolf Virchow.* Berlin: Stapp, 1982.

Blackbourn, David and Geoff Eley. *The Peculiarities of German History.* Oxford: Oxford University Press, 1984.

Blackbourn, David, and Richard J Evans, eds. *The German Bourgeoisie.* London: Routledge, 1991.

Boyd, Byron. 'Rudolf Virchow. The Scientist as Citizen'. Ph.D. Diss., University of North Carolina, 1981.

Bruch, Rüdiger vom, ed. *Weder Kommunismus noch Kapitalismus. Bürgerliche Sozialreform in Deutschland vom Vormarz bis zur Ära Adenauer.* München: C H Beck, 1985.

Bußmann, Walter. 'Rudolf Virchow und der Staat'. In H Berding, ed. *Vom Staat des Ancien Régime zum modernen Parteistaat.* München, 1978.

Dahrendorf, Ralf. *Society and Democracy in Germany.* New York: W W Norton, 1967.

Düding, Dieter. *Der National-Soziale Verein, 1896-1903. Der gescheiterte Versuch einer parteipolitischen Synthese von Nationalismus, Sozialismus und Liberalismus.* München: R Oldenbourg, 1972.

Eisenberg, Leon. 'Rudolf Ludwig Karl Virchow, Where Are You Now That We Need You?', *American Journal of Medicine* 77 (1984): 524–32.

Bibliography

Eley, Geoff. 'Liberalism, Europe, and the Bourgeoisie, 1860-1914'. In Blackbourn and Evans, eds., *The German Bourgeoisie*. 293–317.

Evans, Richard J. *Death in Hamburg*. London: Penguin Books, 1990 [1987].

Finkenrath, Kurt. *Die Medizinalreform*. Leipzig: Johann Ambrosius Barth, 1929.

Fischer, Alfons. *Geschichte des deutschen Gesundheitswesens*. 2 volumes. Berlin: Kommissionsverlag von Oscar Rothacker, 1933.

Frevert, Ute. *Krankheit als politisches Problem*. Göttingen: Vandenhoeck & Ruprecht, 1984.

Göckenjan, Gerd. *Kurieren und Staatmachen. Gesundheit und Medizin in der bürgerlichen Welt*. Frankfurt: Suhrkamp, 1985.

Hamerow, Theodore. *Restoration, Revolution, Reaction*. Princeton: Princeton University Press, 1958.

———. *The Social Foundations of German Unification 1858–1871*. 2 vols. Princeton: Princeton University Press, 1969–72.

Heffter, Heinrich. *Die deutsche Selbstverwaltung*. Stuttgart: K F Koehler, 1950.

Hofmann, Wolfgang. 'Preußische Stadtverordnetenversammlungen als Repräsentativ-Organe'. In Jürgen Reulecke, ed. *Die deutsche Stadt im Industriezeitalter*. Wuppertal: Peter Hammer, 1978.

Holl, Klaus, and Günther Trautmann, eds. *Sozialer Liberalismus*. Göttingen: Vandenhoeck & Ruprecht, 1986.

Huerkamp, Claudia. 'Aerzte und Professionalisierung in Deutschland'. *Geschichte und Gesellschaft* 6 (1980): 349–82.

———. *Der Aufstieg der Aerzte im 19. Jahrhundert*. Göttingen: Vandenhoeck & Ruprecht, 1985.

———. 'The History of Smallpox Vaccination in Germany: A First Step in the Medicalization of the German Public'. *Journal of Contemporary History* 20 (1985): 617–35.

Jarausch, Konrad, and Larry Eugene Jones, eds. *In Search of a Liberal Germany: Studies in the History of German Liberalism from 1789 to the Present*. New York: Berg, 1990.

Jahns, Christa-Maria. *Rudolf Virchow: Auswahlbibliographie*. Berlin: Universittsbibliothek, 1983.

Jütte, Robert, ed. *Geschichte der deutschen Aerzteschaft. Organisierte Berufs- und Gesundheitspolitik im 19. und 20. Jahrhundert*. Köln: Deutsche Aerzte-Verlag, 1997.

Kloppenberg, James. *Uncertain Victory. Social Democracy and Progressivism in European and American Thought*. Oxford: Oxford University Press, 1986.

Krieger, Leonard. *The German Idea of Freedom: History of a Political Tradition*. Boston, 1957.

Kroger, Gertrud. *The Concept of Social Medicine ... in Germany*. Chicago: Julius Rosenwald, 1937.

Ladd, Brian. *Urban Planning and Civic Order in Germany, 1860–1914*. Cambridge: Harvard University Press, 1990.

Lammel, Hans-Ulrich. 'Virchow contra Koch?', *Zeitschrift für die gesamte Hygiene* 28 (1982): 206–10.

Langbein, Fritz. 'Der Werdegang der Berliner Stadtentwässerung'. In Hermann Hahn and Fritz Langbein, eds. *Fünfzig Jahre Berliner Stadtentwsserung, 1878–1928*. Berlin: Metzner, 1928.

Langewiesche, Dieter. *Liberalismus in Deutschland*. Frankfurt: Suhrkamp, 1988.

Lindenlaub, Dieter. *Richtungskämpfe im Verein für Sozialpolitik. Wissenschaft und Sozialpolitik im Kaiserreich vornehmlich vom Beginn des Neuen Kurses bis zum Ausbruch des Ersten Weltkrieges, 1890-1914*. Wiesbaden: Steiner, 1967.

Light, Donald, ed.. *Political Values and Health Care: the German Experience*. Cambridge: MIT Press, 1986.

Lubowitzki, Jutta. *Der Hobrechtplan. Probleme der Berlin Stadtentwicklung*. Berlin, 1990.

Machetanz, Helga. 'Die Duell-Forderung Bismarcks an Virchow im Jahre 1865'. Med. Diss., University of Erlangen-Nürnberg, 1977.

Mazzolini, Renato. *Politisch-biologische Analogien im Frühwerk Rudolf Virchows*. Translated by Klaus-Peter Tieck. Marburg: Basilisken-Presse, 1988.

Mommsen, Wolfgang. *Max Weber and German Politics 1890–1920*. Chicago: University of Chicago Press, 1984 [1974, 1959].

Pflanze, Otto. *Bismarck and the Development of Germany*. Princeton: Princeton University Press, 1963.

Pridian, Daniel. 'Rudolf Virchow and Social Medicine in Historical Perspective'. *Medical History* 8 (1964): 274–8.

Rodgers, Daniel T. *Atlantic Crossings. Social Politics in a Progressive Age*. Cambridge: Harvard University Press, 1998.

Rosen, George. 'What is Social Medicine?', *Bulletin of the History of Medicine* 21 (1947): 674–733.

Schipperges, Heinrich. *Rudolf Virchow*. Reinbek bei Hamburg: Rowohlt, 1994.

Schwalbe, Julius. *Virchow-Bibliographie, 1843–1901*. Berlin: Georg Reimer, 1901.

Sheehan, James. *German Liberalism in the Nineteenth Century*. Chicago: University of Chicago Press, 1978.

———. 'Liberalism and the City in Nineteenth-Century Germany'. *Past and Present* 51 (1971): 116–37.

———. *The Career of Lujo Brentano. A Study of Liberalism and Social Reform in Germany*. Chicago: University of Chicago Press, 1966.

Silver, George. 'Virchow, the Heroic Model in Medicine: Health Policy by Accolade'. *American Journal of Public Health* 77 (1987): 82–8.

Simson, John von. *Kanalisation und Städtehygiene im 19. Jahrhundert*. Düsseldorf: Verein Deutscher Ingenieure, 1983.

Bibliography

Spree, Reinhard. *Health and Social Class in Imperial Germany*. Leamington Spa: Berg, 1988.

Starr, Paul. *The Social Transformation of American Medicine*. New York: Basic Books, 1982.

Stern, Fritz. *The Failure of Illiberalism: Essays on the Political Culture of Modern Germany*. New York: Knopf, 1972.

Stürzbecher, Manfred. 'Rudolf Virchow und die kommunale Gesundheitspolitik in Berlin'. *Verhandlungen der Deutschen Gesellschaft für Pathologie* 68 (1984): xxxiv–xl.

Tampke, Jürgen. 'Bismarck's Social Legislation: A Genuine Breakthrough?', In W J Mommsen and Wolfgang Mock, eds. *The Emergences of the Welfare State in Britain and Germany*. London: Croom Helm, 1981.

Theiner, Peter. *Sozialer Liberalismus und deutsche Weltpolitik: Friedrich Naumann im Wilhelminischen Deutschland (1860–1919)*. Baden-Baden: Nomos, 1983.

Thienel, Ingrid. 'Hobrecht, James'. *Neue Deutsche Biographie*. Berlin: Duncker and Humblot. 280–81.

Thybusch, Anja. 'Rudolf Virchow. Parlamentarische Tätigkeit und Gesundheitspolitik in Reichstag und preussischem Abgeordnetenhaus'. Med. Diss., University of Kiel, 1989.

Tiarks-Jungk, Petra. 'Rudolf Virchows Beiträge zur öffentlichen Gesundheitspflege in Berlin'. Med. Diss., University of Gießen, 1984.

Vasold, Manfred. *Rudolf Virchow: Der große Arzt und Politiker*. Frankfurt: Fischer Taschenbuch Verlag, 1990.

Weber, Max. *From Max Weber: Essays in Sociology*. H H Gerth and C Wright Mills, eds. New York: Oxford University Press, 1946.

Wehler, Hans-Ulrich. *The German Empire, 1871–1918*. Translated by Kim Traynor. Leamington Spa: Berg, 1985.

Weindling, Paul. 'Bourgeois Values, Doctors, and the State: the Professionalization of Medicine in Germany, 1848–1933'. In Blackbourn and Evans, eds., *The German Bourgeoisie*. 198–223.

———. *Health, Race, and German Politics between National Unification and Nazism, 1870–1945*. Cambridge: Cambridge University Press, 1989.

———. 'Was Social Medicine Revolutionary? Rudolf Virchow and the Revolution of 1848'. *Bulletin of the Society for the Social History of Medicine* 34 (1984): 13–18.

Winter, Kurt. *Rudolf Virchow*. Leipzig: Urania-Verlag, 1956.

Zimmerman, Andrew. 'Anti-Semitism as Skill: Rudolf Virchow's *Schulstatistik* and the Racial Composition of Germany'. *Central European History* 32 (1999): 409–29.

Index